HOW TO DRAW FOR 6-8 YEAR OLDS

Learn to Draw Cute Animals, Gifts, Magical Things, and Other Cool Stuff

Book for Kids Age 6+

Anna Robin

Published by: Bemberton Ltd

ISBN: 978-1-915833-49-5

Disclaimer
This book is for fun and learning how to draw. The information is general and not professional advice. The author and publisher are not responsible for any actions taken based on the content of this book.

View all our books at **bemberton.com**

What's Inside

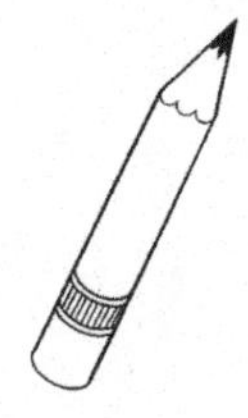

5 Let's Get Drawing!

9 Cute Animals

23 Sea Creatures

37 Fantasy

49 Everyday Objects

63 Space

77 Vehicles

91 Nature

This Book Belongs to

Let's Get Drawing!

Imagine creating your own amazing pictures, just like the ones in your favorite books and cartoons. Guess what? You can!

In this book, you'll learn how to draw all sorts of cool stuff—from cute animals to awesome cars and even magical sea creatures. There are more than 50 fun things to draw, so you're sure to find something you'll love.

Don't worry if you're not sure where to begin—we're here to help you every step of the way. All you need is some simple tools and your imagination.

What You'll Need:

- **A Pencil:** Think of it as your magic wand that brings your drawings to life!
- **An Eraser:** Even wizards make mistakes. Your eraser is here to help fix them.
- **A Sharpener:** Keep your pencil sharp and ready to go.
- **Some Paper:** Any kind will do, but a sketchbook is extra special.

- **Crayons or Colored Pencils:** These will add a splash of color to your drawings.
- **Your Imagination:** This is the most important tool of all! With your imagination, you can create anything you dream of.

How to Use This Book

Drawing is all about having fun and letting your creativity shine. There's no right or wrong way, so just enjoy making your art!

- **Follow the Steps:** We'll show you each step with bold lines for what to add next. The lighter lines show what you've already drawn.
- **Erase as You Go:** When you see dashed lines, that's your cue to erase them to make your picture look just right.
- **Practice Makes Perfect:** There's space in the book for you to practice. Once you've filled it up, grab some paper and keep drawing! See how much you improve each time!
- **Add Some Color:** Once you've finished your drawing, grab your crayons or colored pencils and make it colorful!

Let's start with something simple — a cool 3D Bubble Number 6:

1.

2.

3.

4.

5.

6.

Remove extra lines

Some finishing touches. Ta-Da!

Great job! How did it go? Take a look at your drawing — what do you like best about it?

If you want, you can add some color or try drawing it again. Remember, the more you practice, the better you get! Don't be afraid to make mistakes; they're part of the learning process. And remember, every drawing is unique and special, just like you!

Here are some handy tips to help you with the next drawings:

- **Take Your Time:** No rush — enjoy each step.
- **Love Your Drawing:** Wobbly lines make it unique.
- **Practice Makes Progress:** The more you draw, the better you'll get.
- **Make It Yours:** Use your imagination to add your own twist.
- **Have Fun:** The most important part is having fun!

Ready to begin? Turn the page, pick a drawing, and let the adventure begin!

Cute Animals

Kitten

Kittens are so tiny when they're born that they keep their eyes closed. They don't open them until they're about a week old. This keeps their eyes safe while they grow.

1.

2.

3.

4.

5.

Add details

6.

Remove extra lines

Some finishing touches. Ta-Da!

Sausage Dog

Sausage dogs are funny little dogs with long bodies, which is why people also call them "wiener dogs." They look a bit like hot dogs!

1.

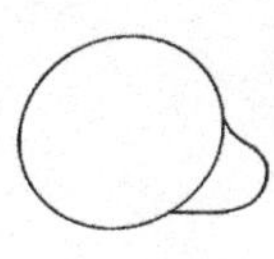

2.

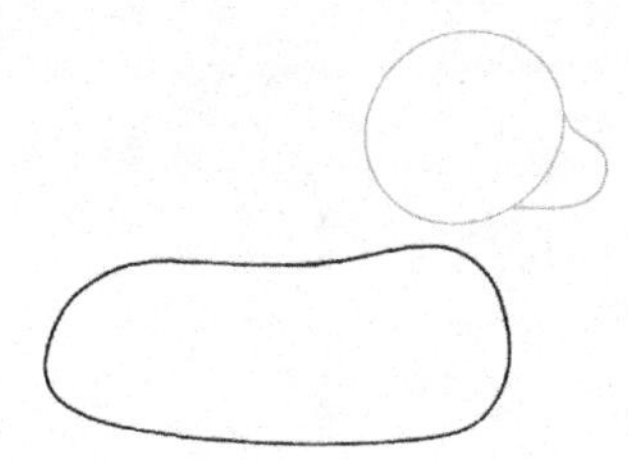

3.

4.

5.

6.

Some finishing touches. Ta-Da!

Elephant

Elephants love to play in the water, and they're really good swimmers! When they swim, they can use their long trunks like a snorkel. This helps them breathe even when most of their body is underwater.

1.

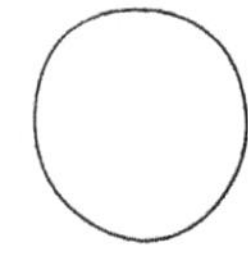

2.

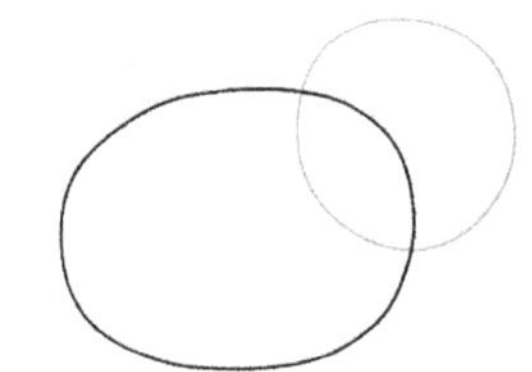

3.

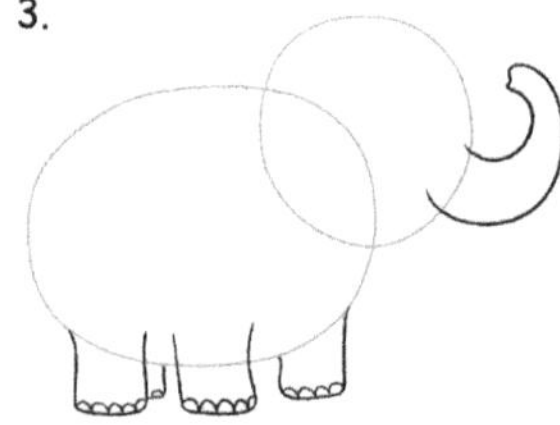

4.

5.

6.

Some finishing touches.
Ta-Da!

Bumblebee

Honey comes from bees! They make it by collecting nectar from flowers and then turning it into sweet, sticky honey. Bees store this honey in their hive.

1.

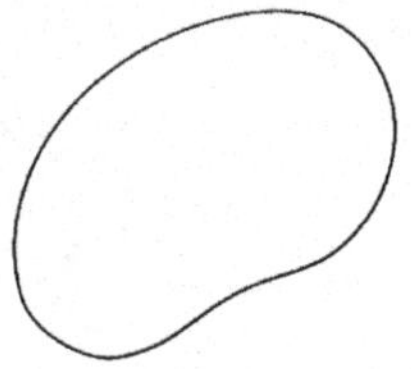

2.

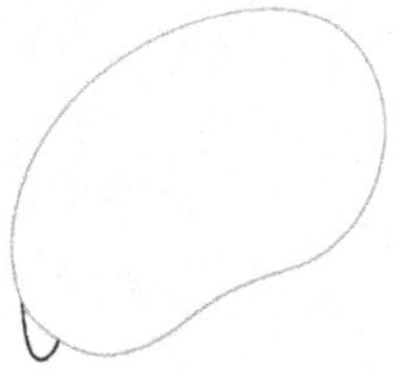

3.

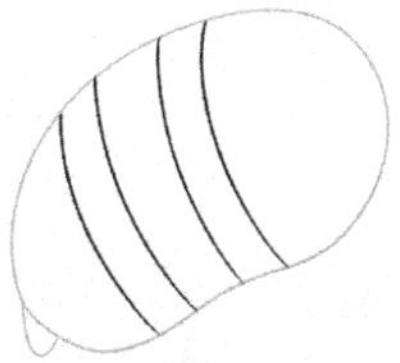

4.

5.

6.

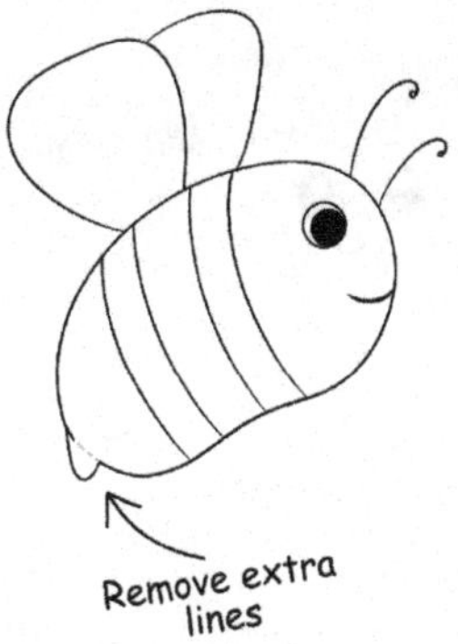

Remove extra lines

Colour in Stripes!

Caterpillar

Caterpillars are eating machines! They spend most of their time munching leaves and can eat hundreds of times their own weight in a single day.

1.

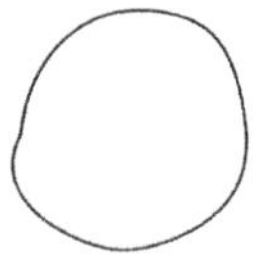

2.

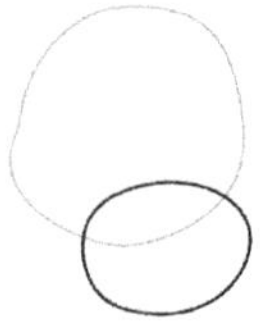

3.

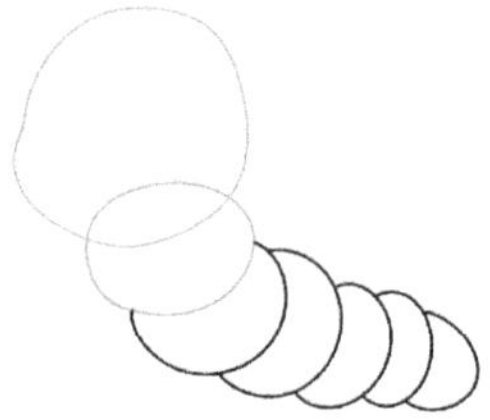

4.

5. Add details

6. Remove extra lines

Some finishing touches. Ta-Da!

Sheep

Sheep have thick woolly coats. They spend most of their day eating grass and staying close together in groups called flocks.

1.

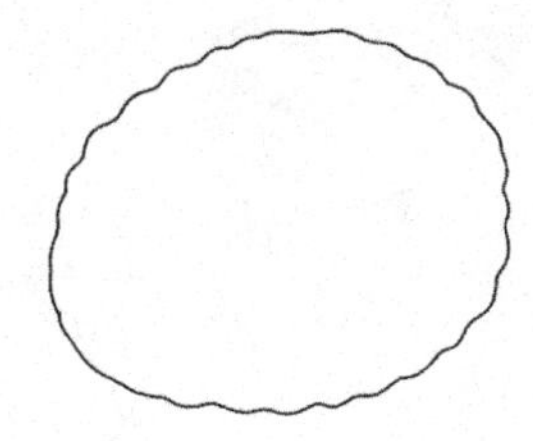

2.

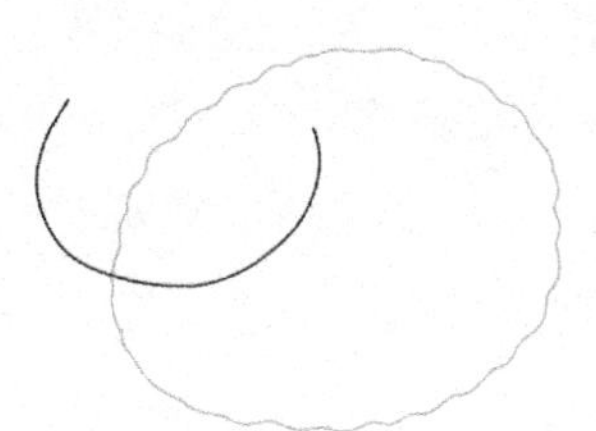

3.

4.

5.

6.

Some finishing touches. Ta-Da!

Cow

Cows are amazing because they produce milk, which is used to make cheese, butter, ice cream, and, of course, the milk you drink!

1.

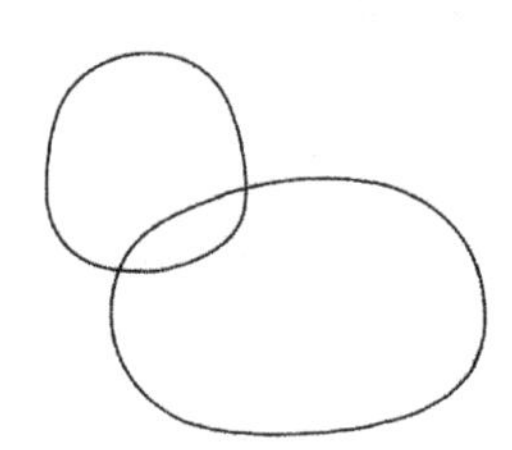

2.

3.

4.

5.

6.

Some finishing touches.
Ta-Da!

Giraffe

Giraffes have long necks so they can reach leaves high up in trees. This helps them eat food that other animals can't reach. Their long necks also help them see far away!

1.

2.

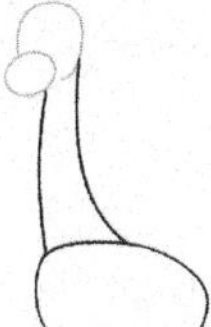

3.

4.

5.

6.

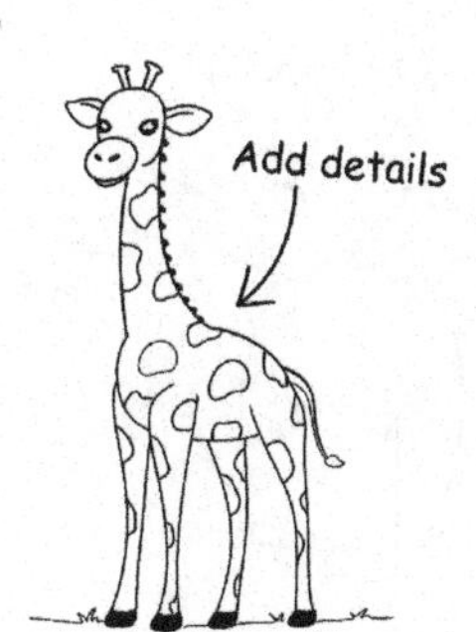

Fox

Foxes are clever animals. They live in forests, fields, and even cities. Foxes are good at sneaking around quietly and are great hunters.

1.

2.

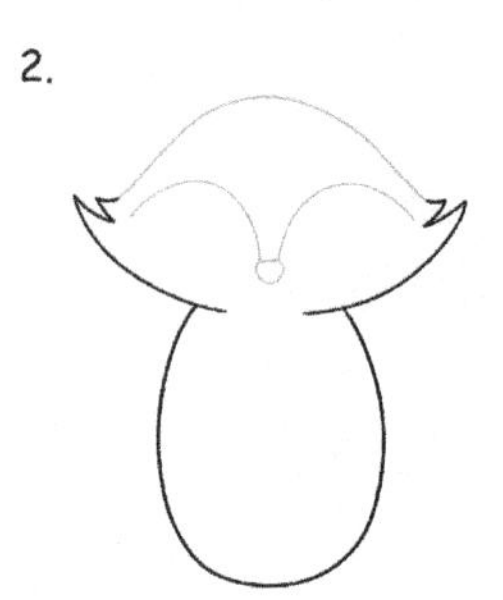

3.

4.

5.

6.

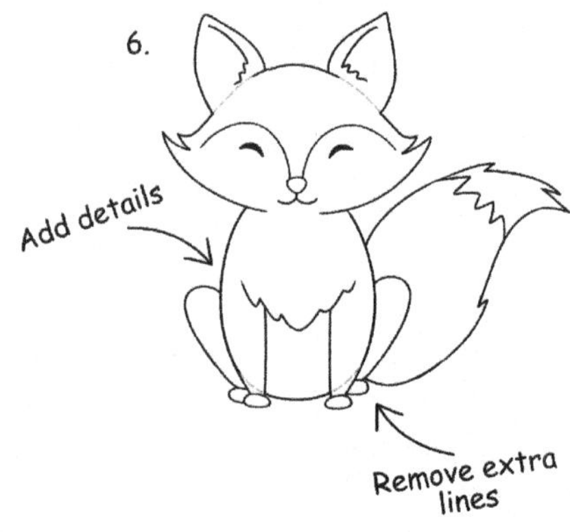

Lion

Lions are known for their big, loud roars that can be heard from up to 5 miles away! Perhaps they're shouting, "I'm the king of the jungle!"

1.

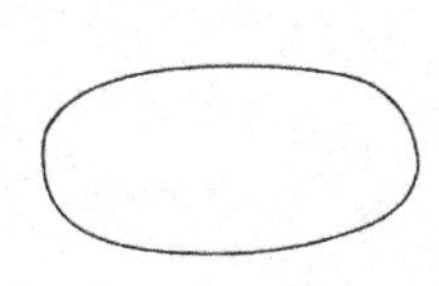

2.

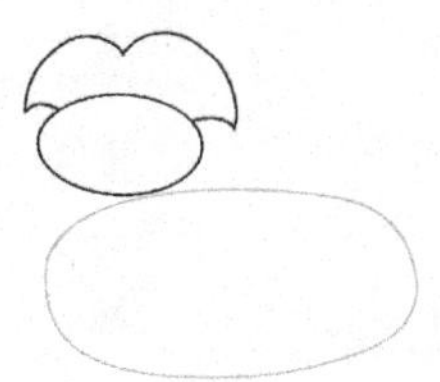

3.

4.

5.

6.

Some finishing touches.
Ta-Da!

Now it's your turn

Now it's your turn

Sea Creatures

Starfish

No Brain, No Problem! Did you know that starfish don't have a brain? Instead, they use their tiny nerves spread across their arms to help them move and find food.

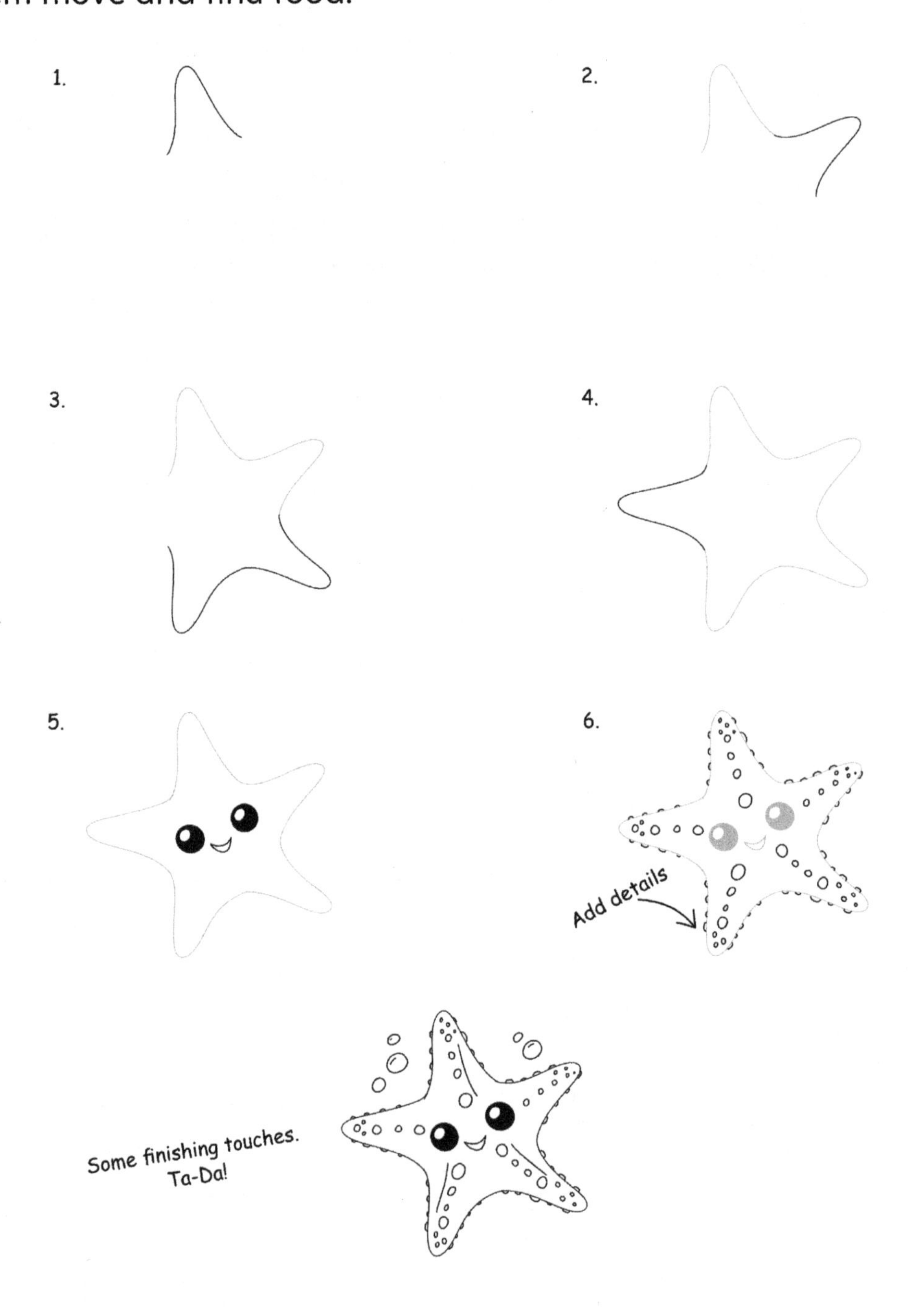

Jellyfish

Jellyfish have been around for over 500 million years, which means they were swimming in the oceans even before the dinosaurs existed!

1.

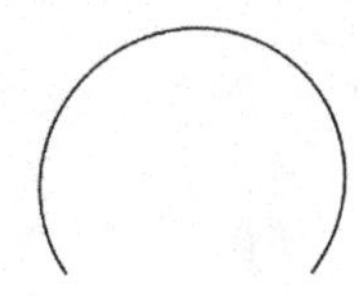

2.

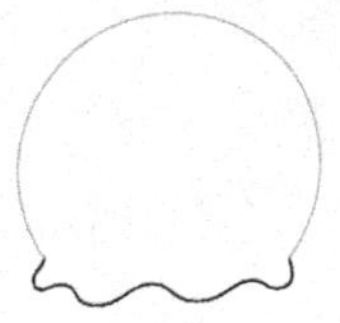

3.

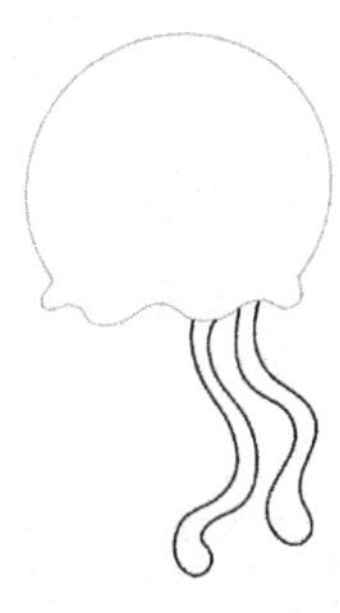

4.

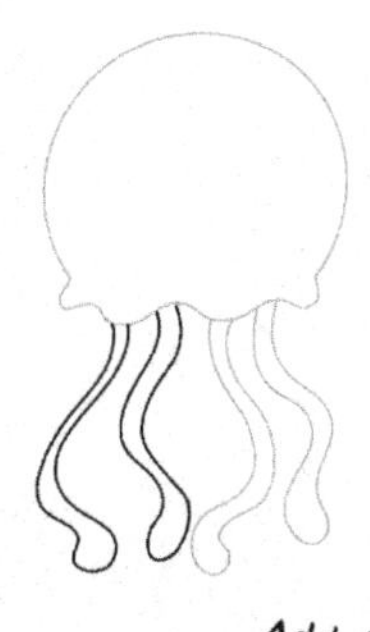

5.

6.

Add details

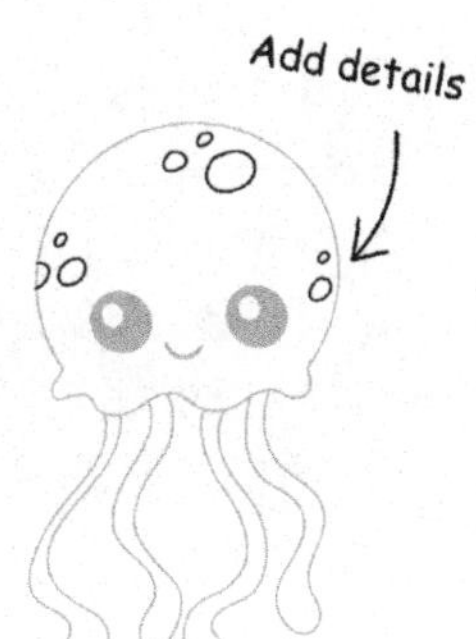

Some finishing touches.
Ta-Da!

Seahorse

Male seahorses carry the babies! The dad seahorse has a special pouch where the mom lays her eggs, and he takes care of them until they hatch.

1.

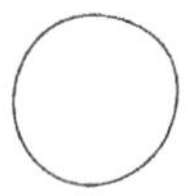

2.

3.

4.

5.

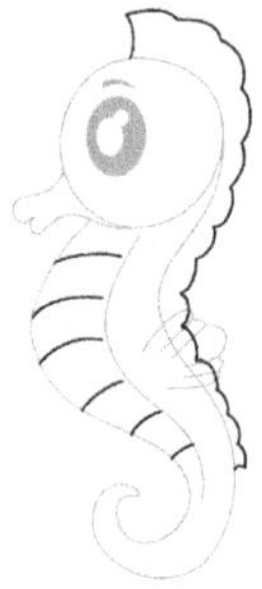

6.

Remove extra lines

Add details

Clownfish

Clownfish became famous because of the movie: Finding Nemo! The main character, Nemo, is a clownfish.

1.

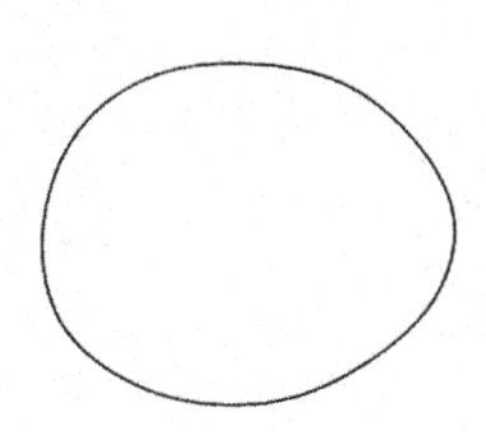

2.

3.

4.

5.

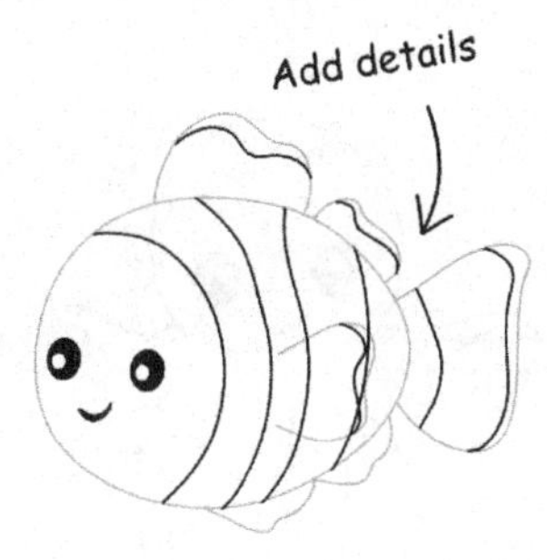

6.

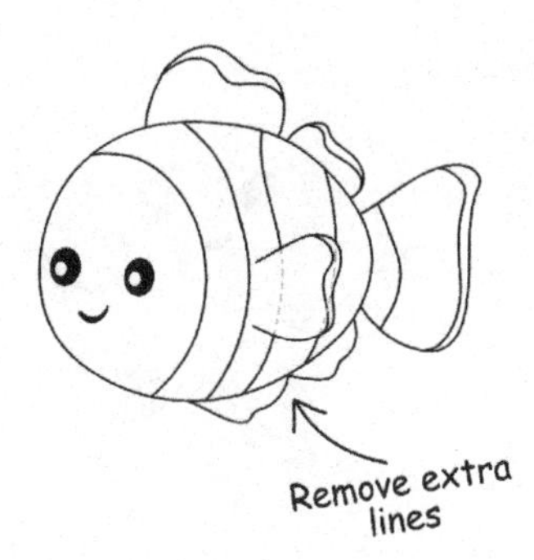

Some finishing touches.
Ta-Da!

Octopus

An octopus has eight arms, and each one is super strong! It can squeeze through tiny spaces to escape or find food. If it loses an arm, it can even grow a new one!

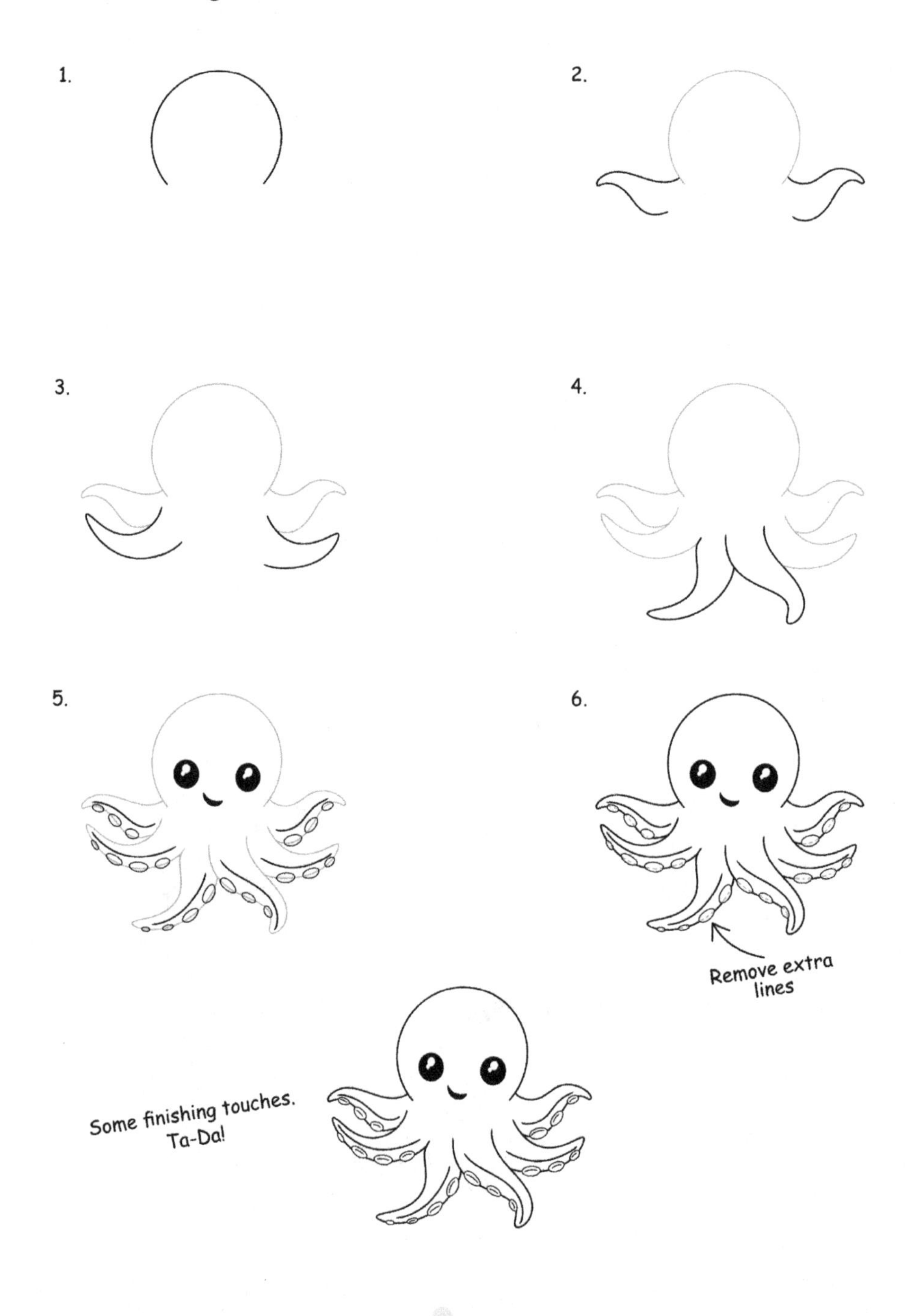

Crab

Crabs are famous for walking sideways! They also have powerful claws for catching food, defending themselves, and communicating with other crabs.

1.

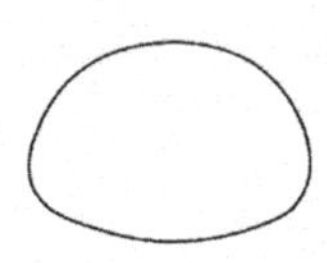

2.

3.

4.

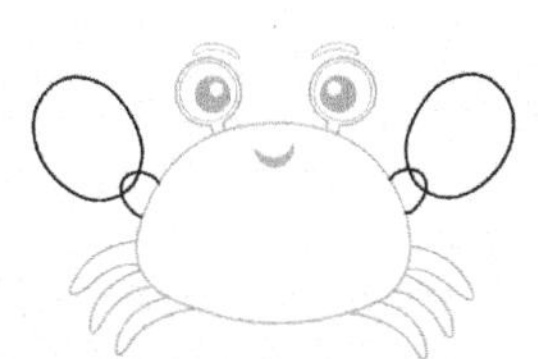

5.

6.

Some finishing touches. Ta-Da!

Dolphin

Dolphins are incredibly intelligent! They can solve problems, play games, and even use tools. They communicate using a series of clicks, whistles, and body language.

1.

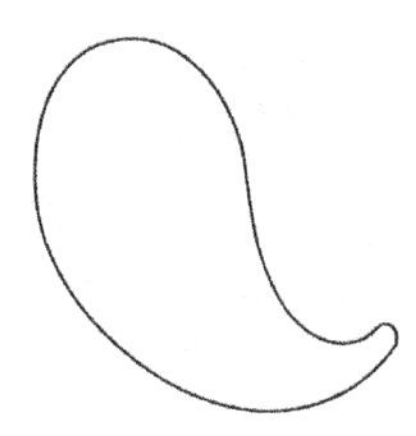

2.

3.

4.

5.

6.

Some finishing touches. Ta-Da!

Turtle

Turtles carry their homes on their backs! Their shells are made of over 50 bones, and they're super strong. The shell protects them, and they can even hide inside it if they feel scared.

1.

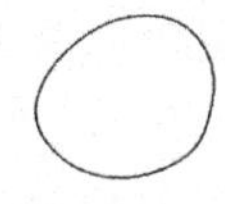

2.

3.

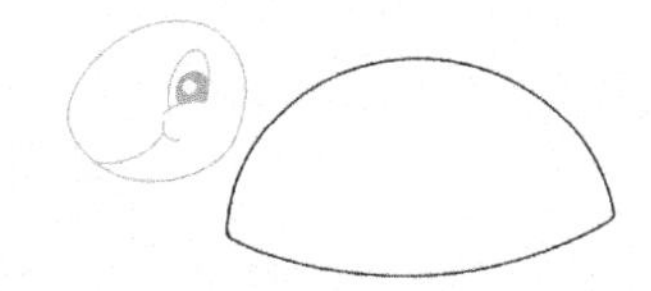

4.

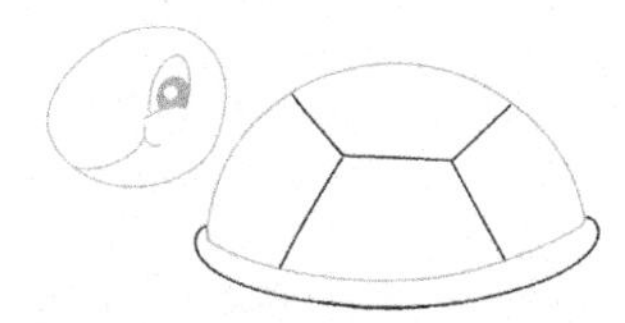

5.

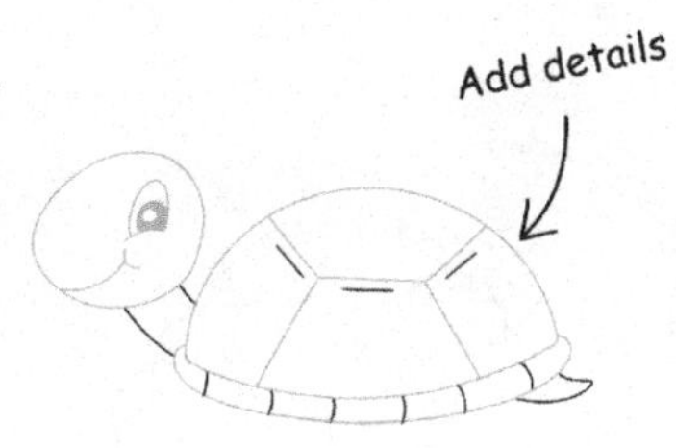

6.

Shell

Shells are like armor for sea creatures like snails, clams, and crabs. These creatures grow shells to protect themselves from predators and rough ocean waves. Each shell is unique, just like our fingerprints!

1.

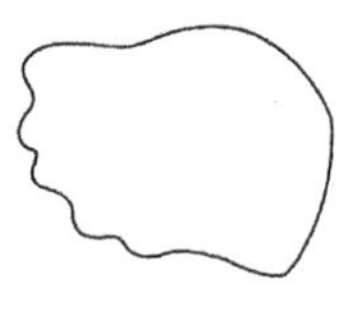

2.

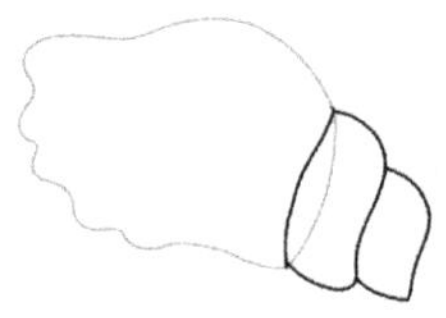

3.

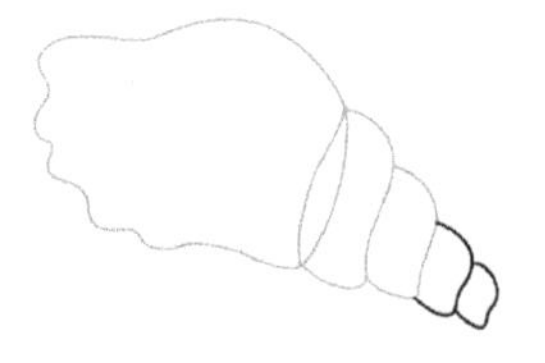

4.

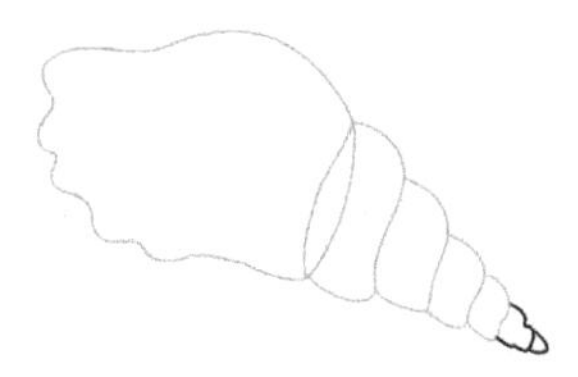

5.

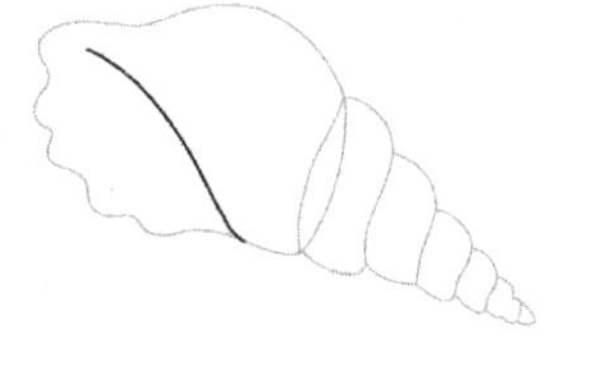

6.

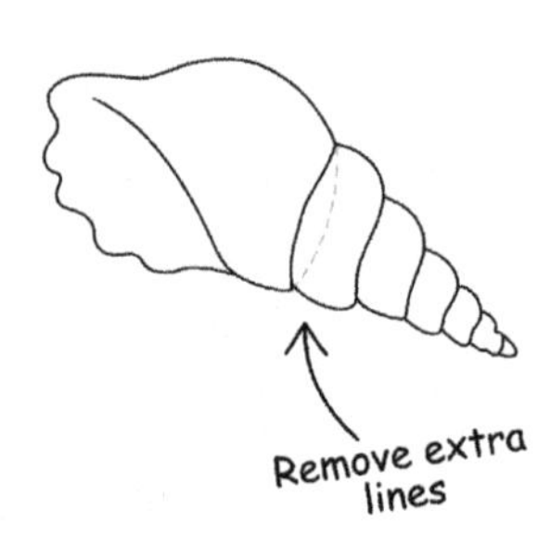

Some finishing touches. Ta-Da!

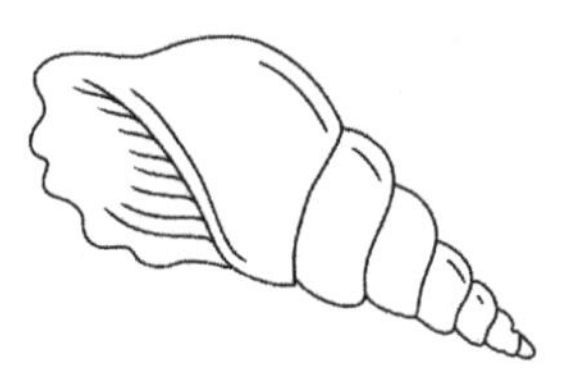

Shark

Sharks can have thousands of teeth in their lifetime! They lose and replace their teeth throughout their lives. Some sharks can lose up to 30,000 teeth in their lifetime.

1.

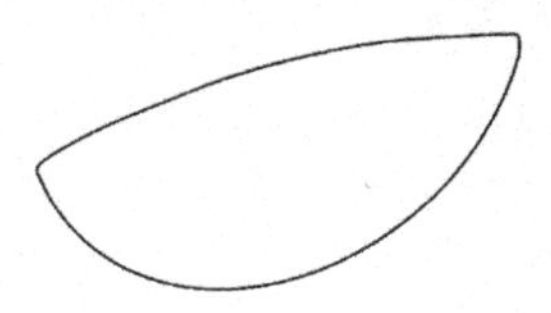

2.

3.

4.

5.

6.

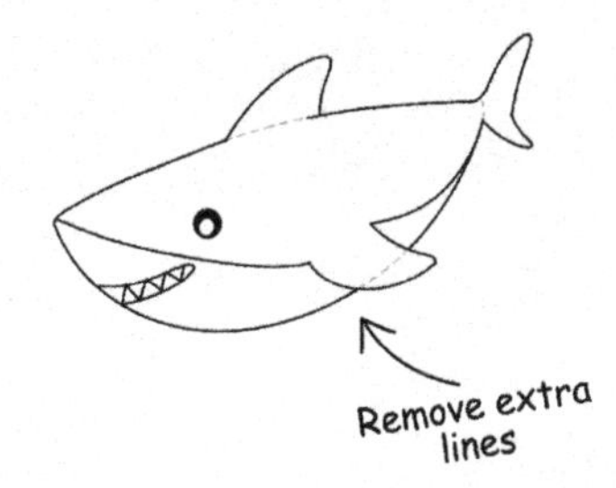

Some finishing touches. Ta-Da!

Now it's your turn

Now it's your turn

Fantasy

Castle

Castles were built a long time ago to protect kings, queens, and their people from enemies. They were like big forts with thick walls and towers, making it hard for attackers to get in.

1.

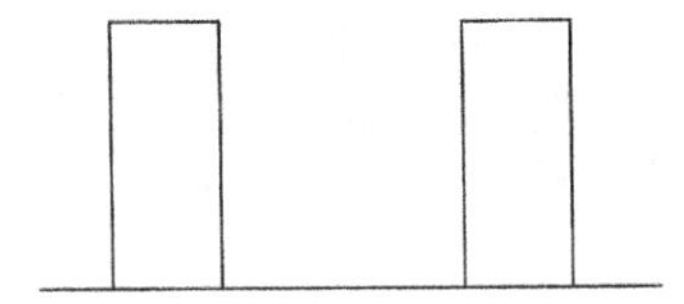

2.

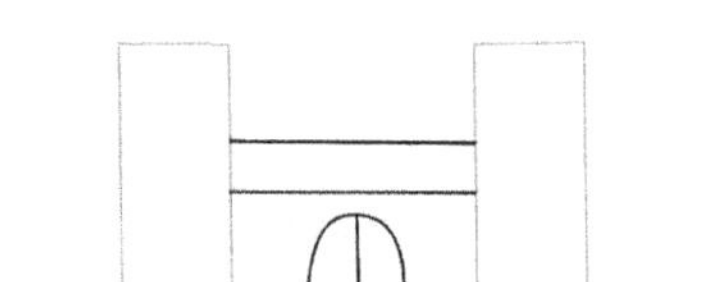

3.

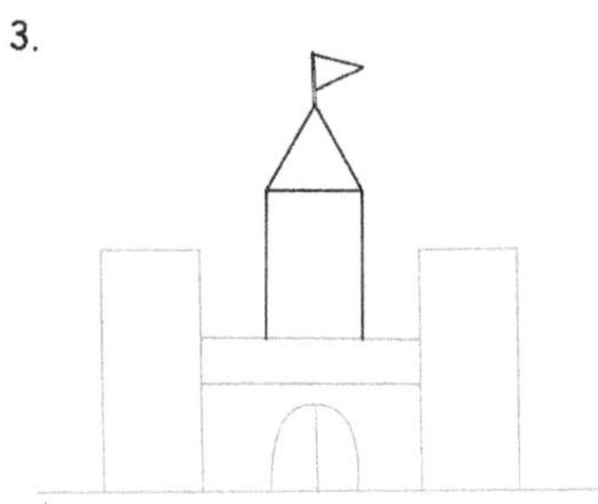

4.

5.

6.

Dragon

Dragons are amazing creatures found in stories and legends from all around the world! Some breathe fire, while others can fly or swim.

1.

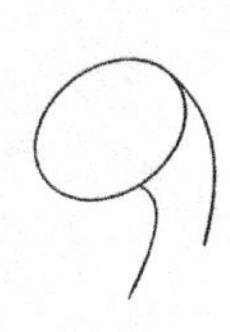

2.

3.

4.

5.

6.

Fairy

Fairies are often imagined as small, magical creatures with wings. They are known for their ability to fly and magical powers, including helping plants grow or granting wishes!

1.

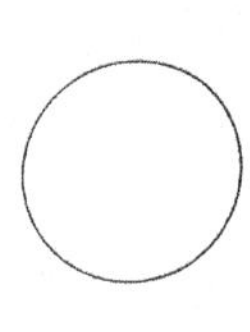

2.

3.

4.

5.

6.

Some finishing touches.
Ta-Da!

Knight

Knights were warriors in the Middle Ages who often fought for their kings and queens. They wore shiny metal armor to protect themselves in battle, that was often decorated with their family's coat of arms.

1.

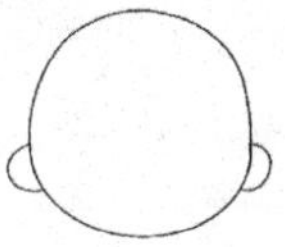

2.

3.

4.

5.

6.

Remove extra lines

Some finishing touches. Ta-Da!

Wizard

Wizards are known for casting spells and using magical objects like wands, potions, and enchanted books. They can make incredible things happen with just a wave of their hand!

1.

2.

3.

4.

5.

6.

Some finishing touches. Ta-Da!

Unicorn

Unicorns are magical horse-like animals with a single horn on their foreheads. They have been part of myths and legends in many cultures for thousands of years.

Mermaid

Mermaids have the upper body of a person and the tail of a fish, which allows them to swim gracefully through the ocean.

1.

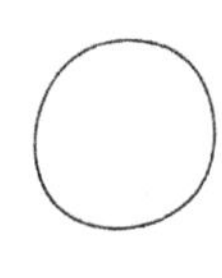

2.

3.

4.

5.

6.

Some finishing touches.
Ta-Da!

Monster

Monsters often appear in stories and legends. They come in all shapes and sizes, from giant sea monsters to tiny naughty ones. These creatures are usually invented to make stories exciting and to teach lessons.

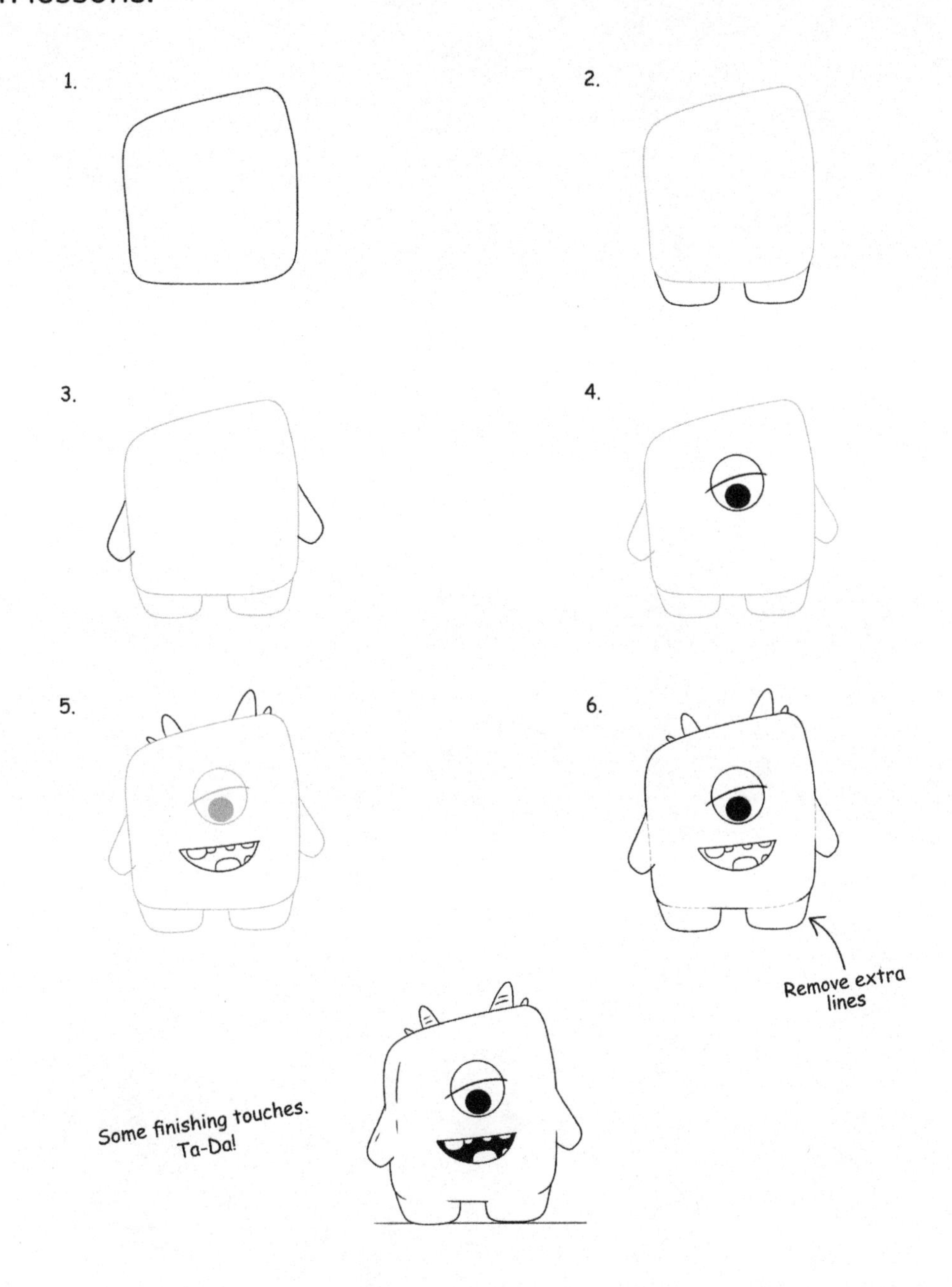

Now it's your turn

Now it’s your turn

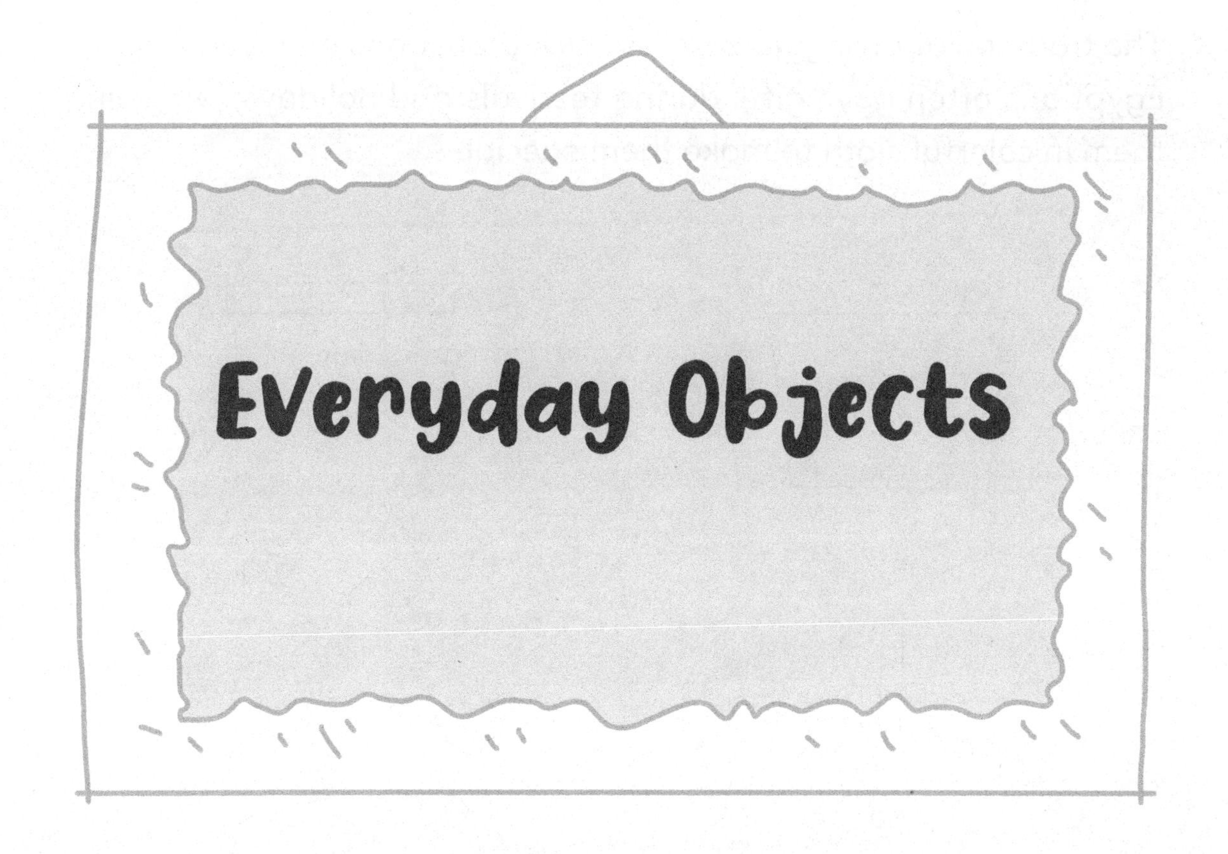
Everyday Objects

Gift Box

The tradition of giving gifts dates back thousands of years! Ancient Egyptians often gave gifts during festivals and holidays, wrapping them in colorful cloth to make them special.

1.

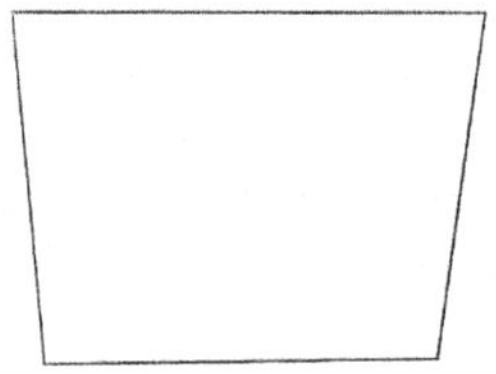

2.

3.

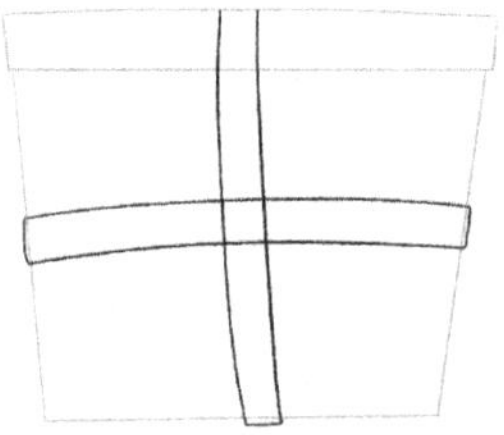

4.

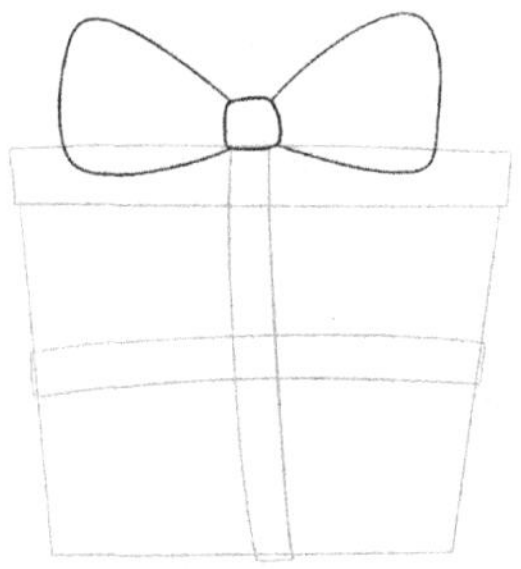

5.

6.

Remove extra lines

Some finishing touches. Ta-Da!

Teddy Bear

The teddy bear was created in the early 1900s! It was named after US President Theodore "Teddy" Roosevelt, who famously refused to shoot a bear during a hunting trip. Soon after, toy makers started making stuffed bears to honor him.

Ice Cream Sundae

An ice cream sundae is a yummy treat made by putting scoops of ice cream in a bowl and adding lots of tasty toppings. You can add things like chocolate sauce, whipped cream, sprinkles, and even a cherry on top.

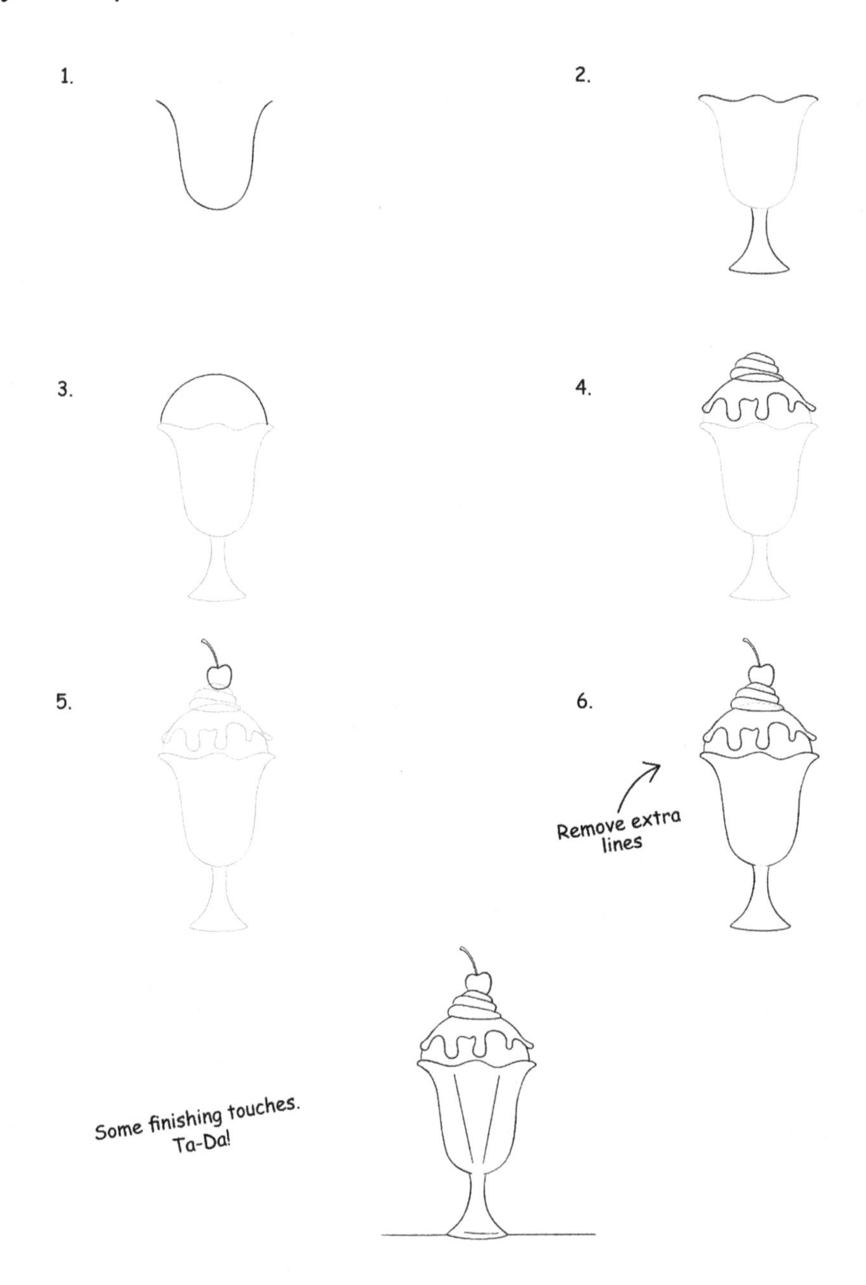

Toy Blocks

One of the most famous types of toy blocks is LEGO. The first LEGO brick was made in 1958 in Denmark, and now, LEGO is loved all over the world. In fact, there are more LEGO bricks in the world than there are people!

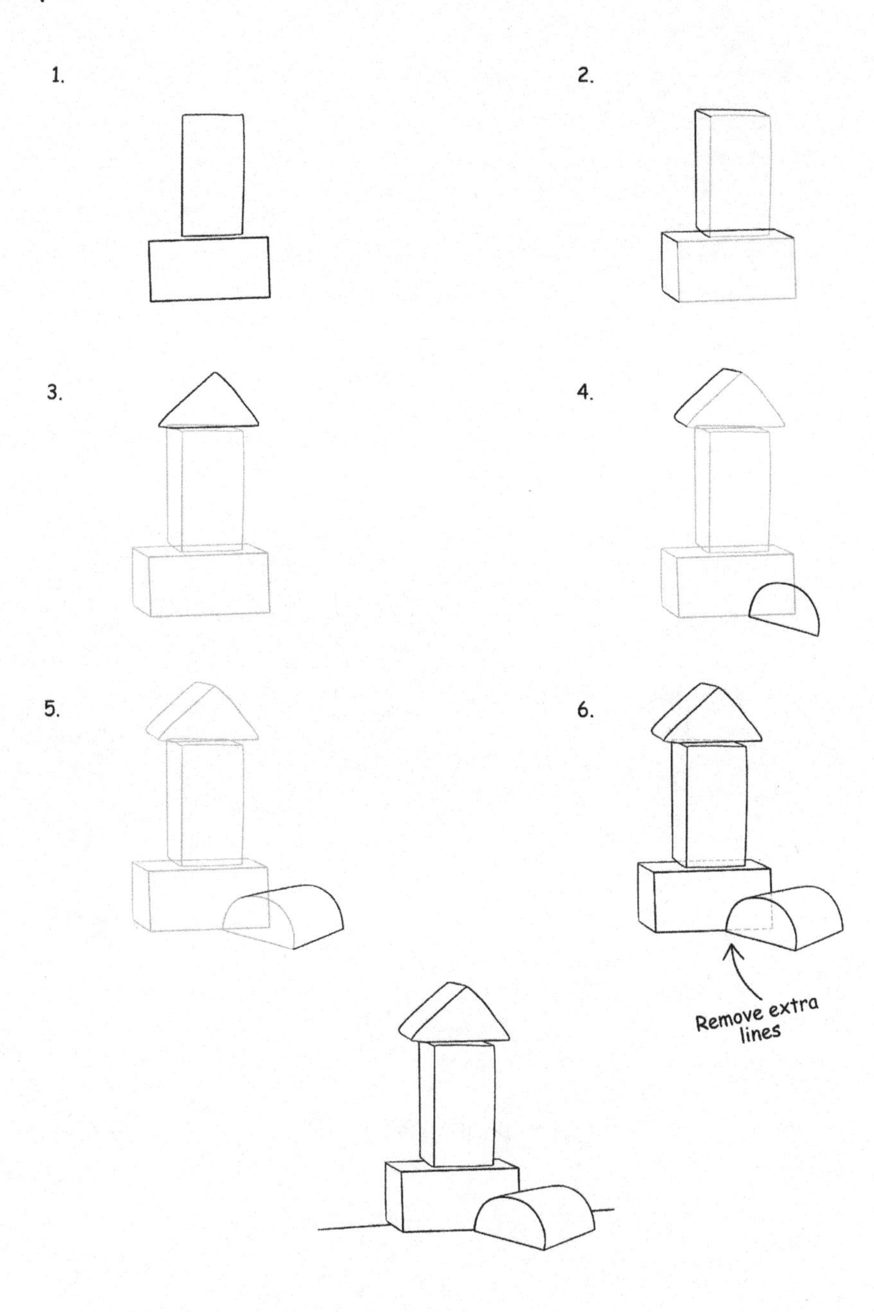

Umbrella with Raindrops

Umbrellas were invented over 4,000 years ago! The first umbrellas were made in ancient Egypt and China and provided shade from the sun. Today, we use them to stay dry in the rain and to protect ourselves from the sun.

1.

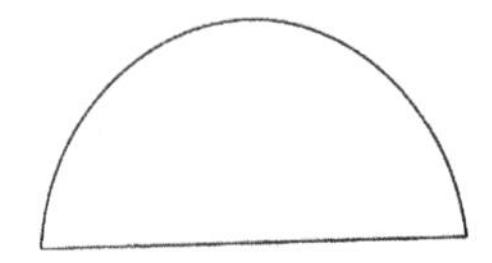

2.

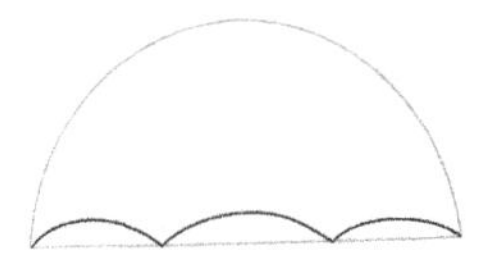

3.

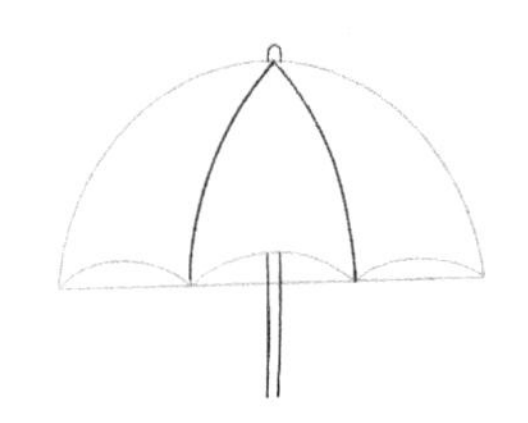

4.

5.

6.

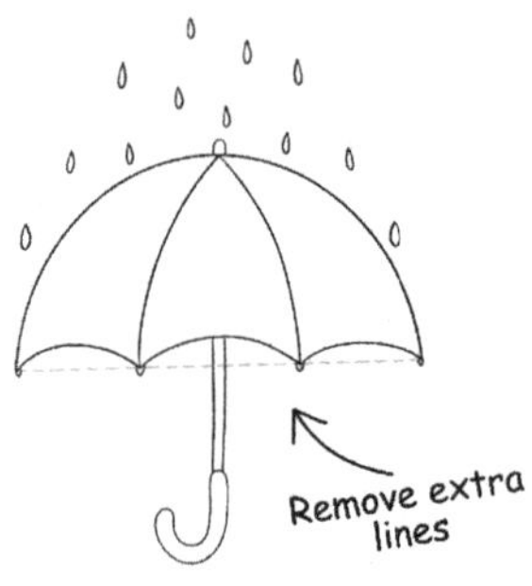

Cap

One of the most popular types of caps is the baseball cap. Baseball players started wearing them long ago to shield their eyes from the sun while playing.

1.

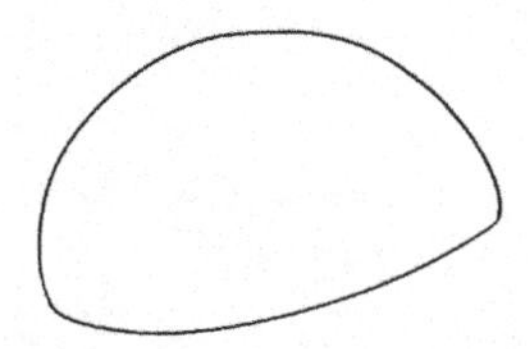

2.

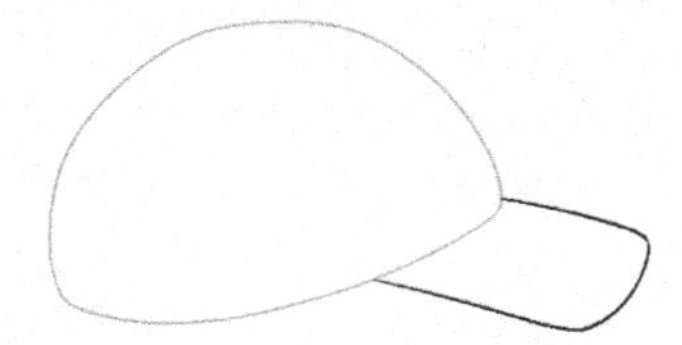

3.

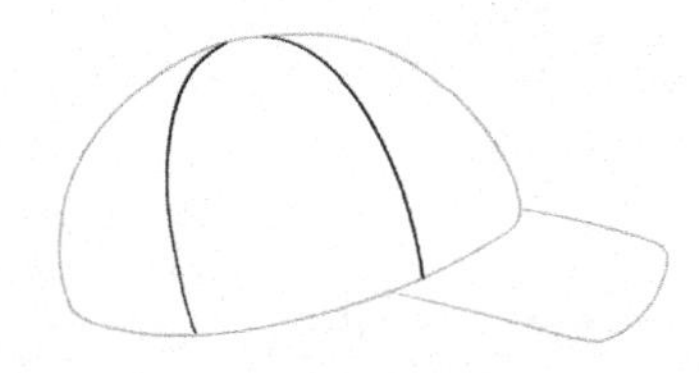

4.

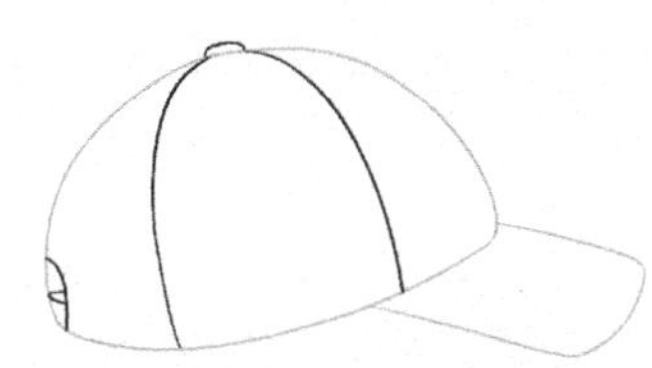

5.

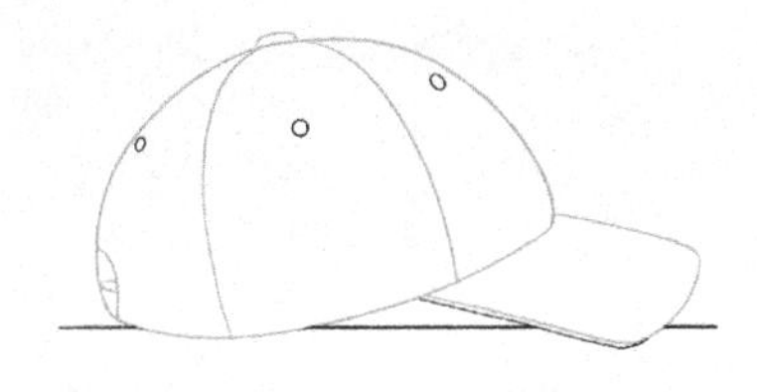

6.

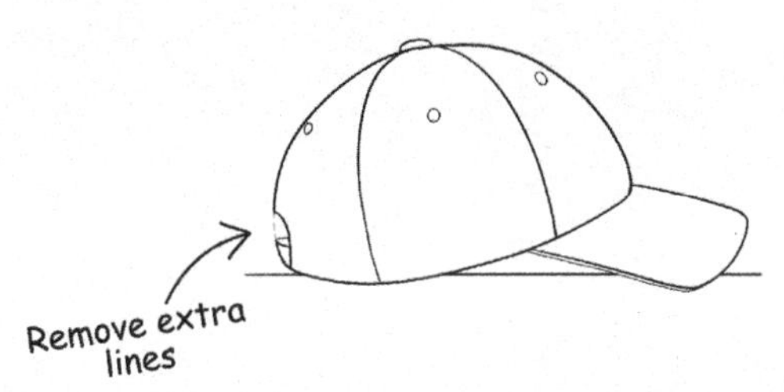

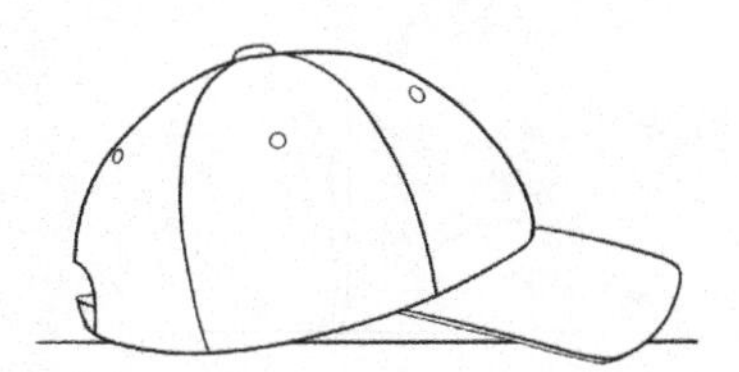

Ball

Ever wonder why a basketball bounces so high? It's because it's filled with air inside! When you push the ball down, the air inside pushes back, making the ball bounce back up. The rubbery outside helps it bounce even higher.

1.

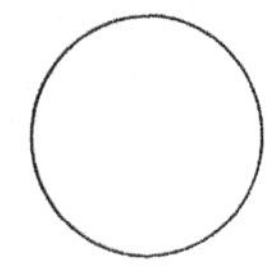

2.

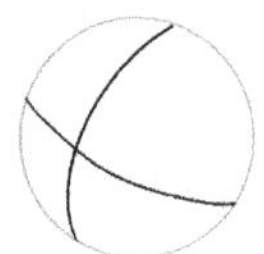

3.

4.

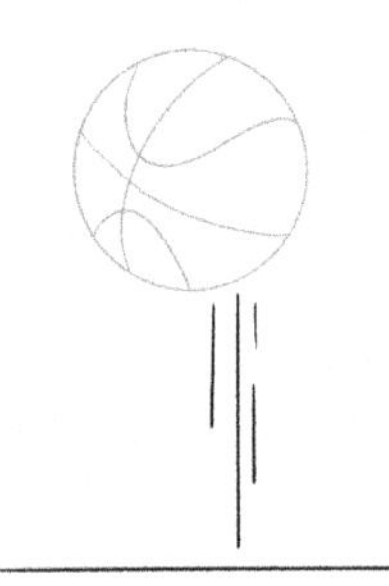

5.

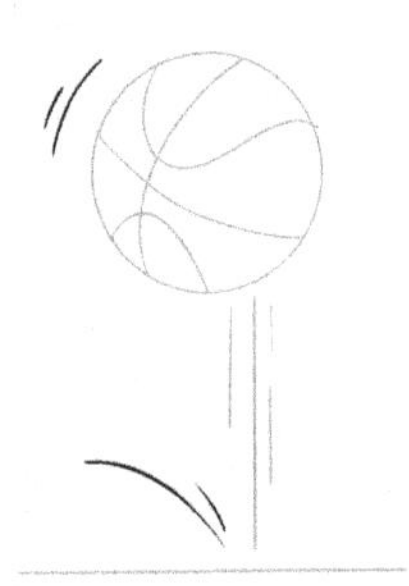

6.

Cup and Saucer

Tea is made by pouring hot water over dried leaves to make a tasty drink. In some countries, like England, people have a special time in the afternoon just for drinking tea, and they call it “tea time.”

Book

Chances are your books are made of paper, just like this one. But did you know the first books weren't made of paper? Long ago, people wrote on clay tablets, animal skins, and tree bark!

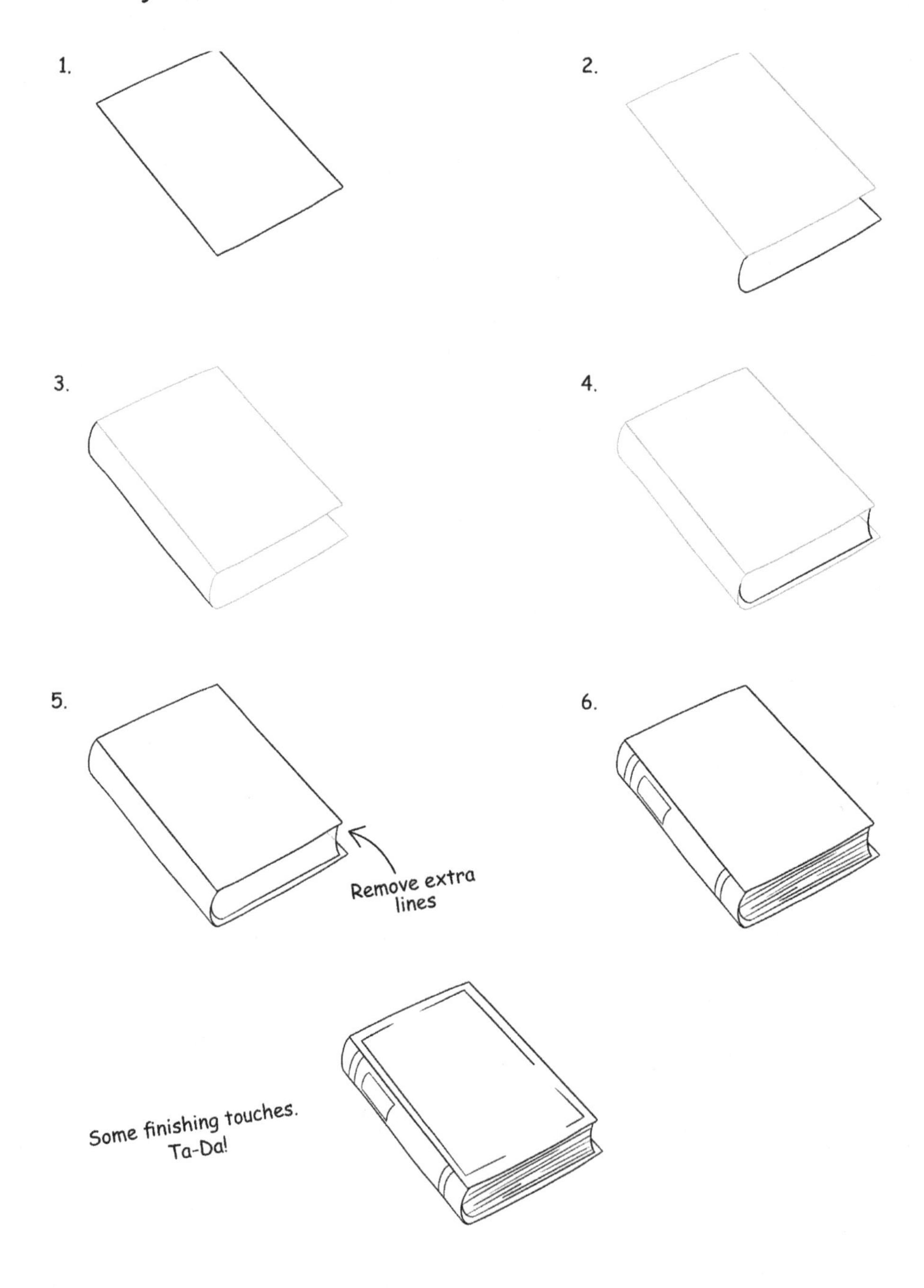

Now it's your turn

Now it's your turn

Now it's your turn

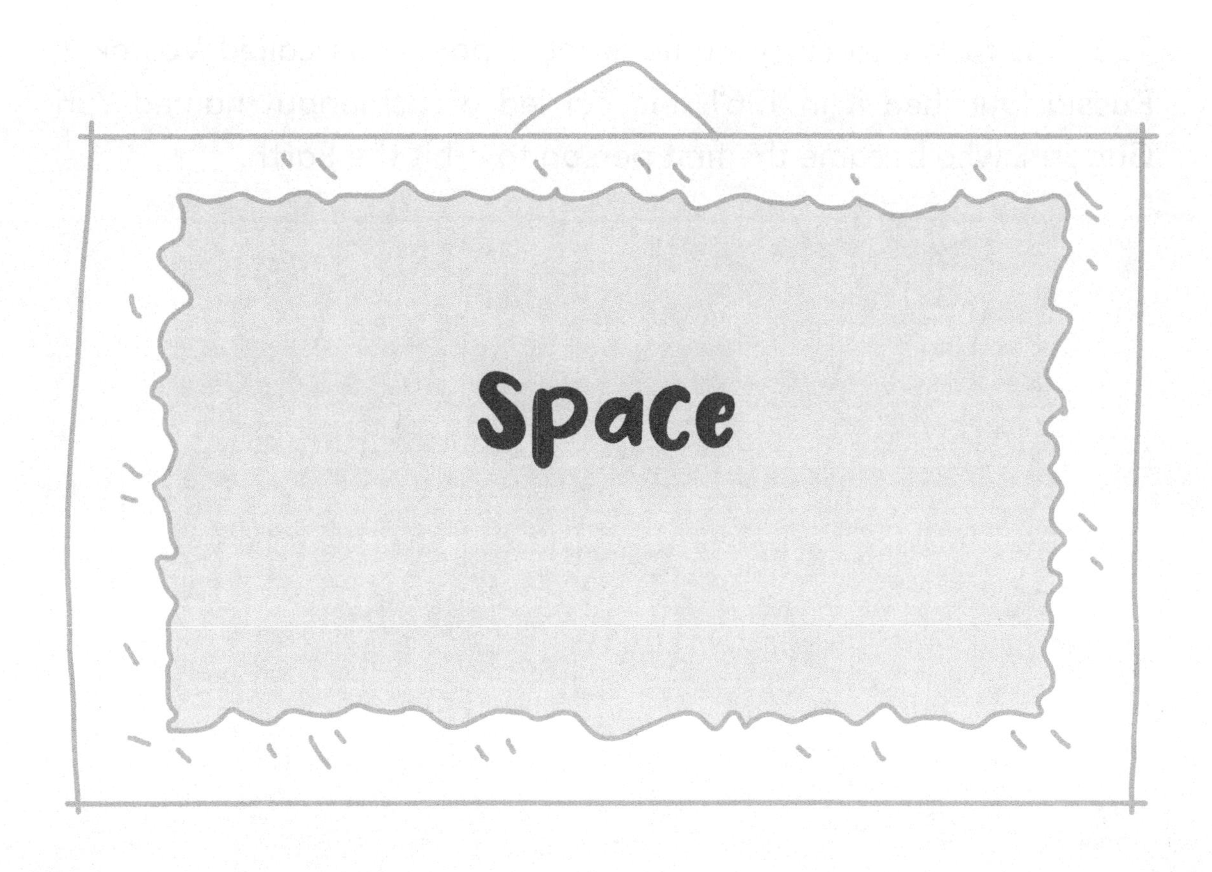
Space

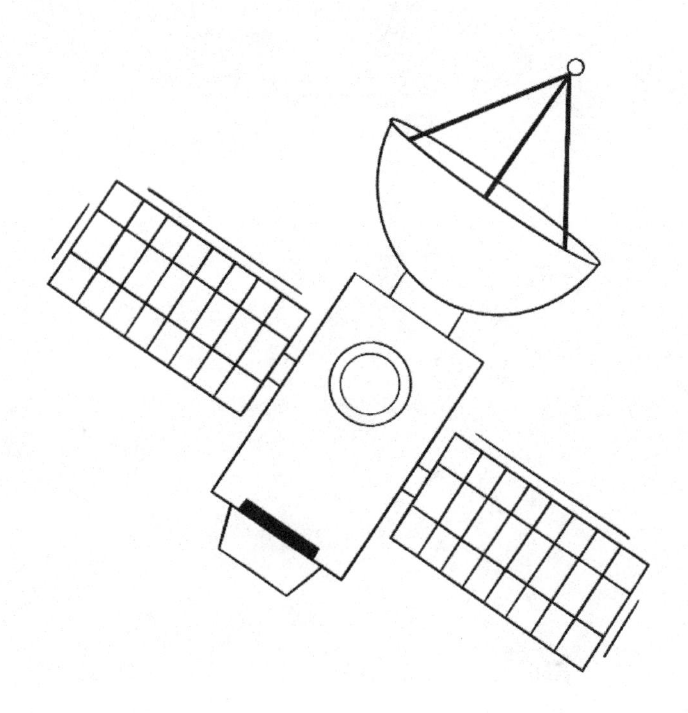

Rocket

The first rocket to carry humans into space was called Vostok 1. Russia launched it in 1961 and carried a cosmonaut named Yuri Gagarin, who became the first person to orbit the Earth.

1.

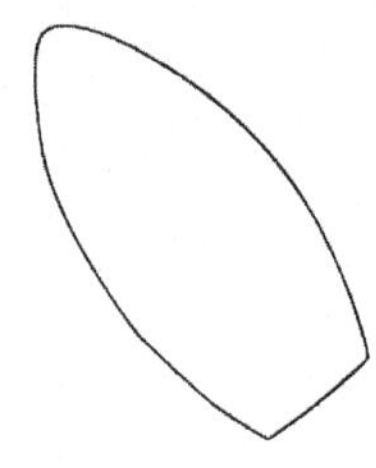

2.

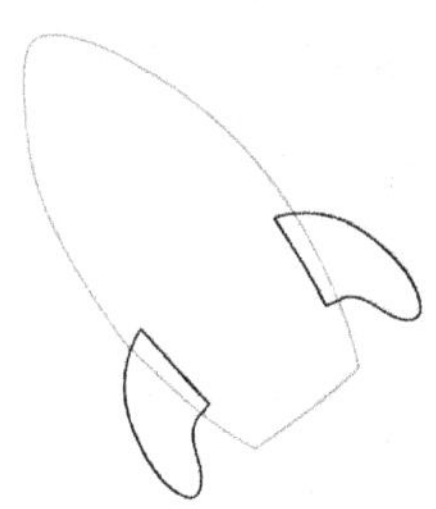

3.

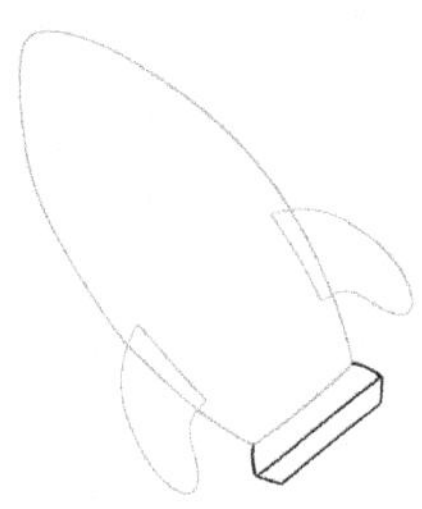

4.

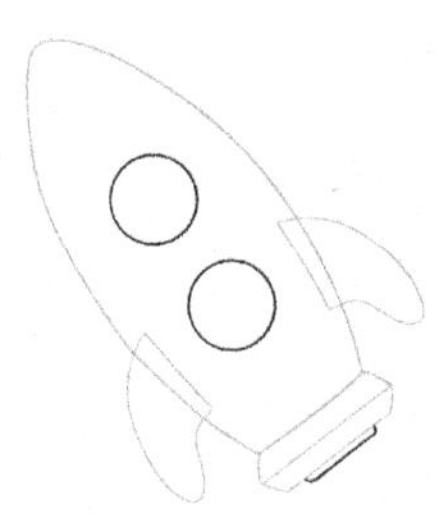

5.

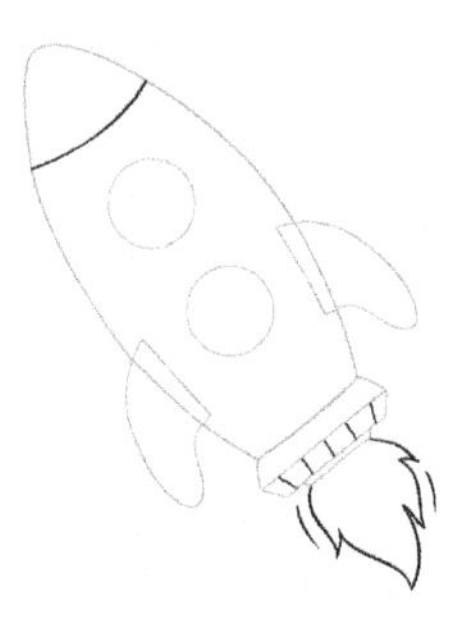

6.

Some finishing touches. Ta-Da!

Astronaut

Astronauts live and work on the International Space Station (ISS), which is like a small house in space! They do experiments, grow plants, and exercise to stay healthy in zero gravity.

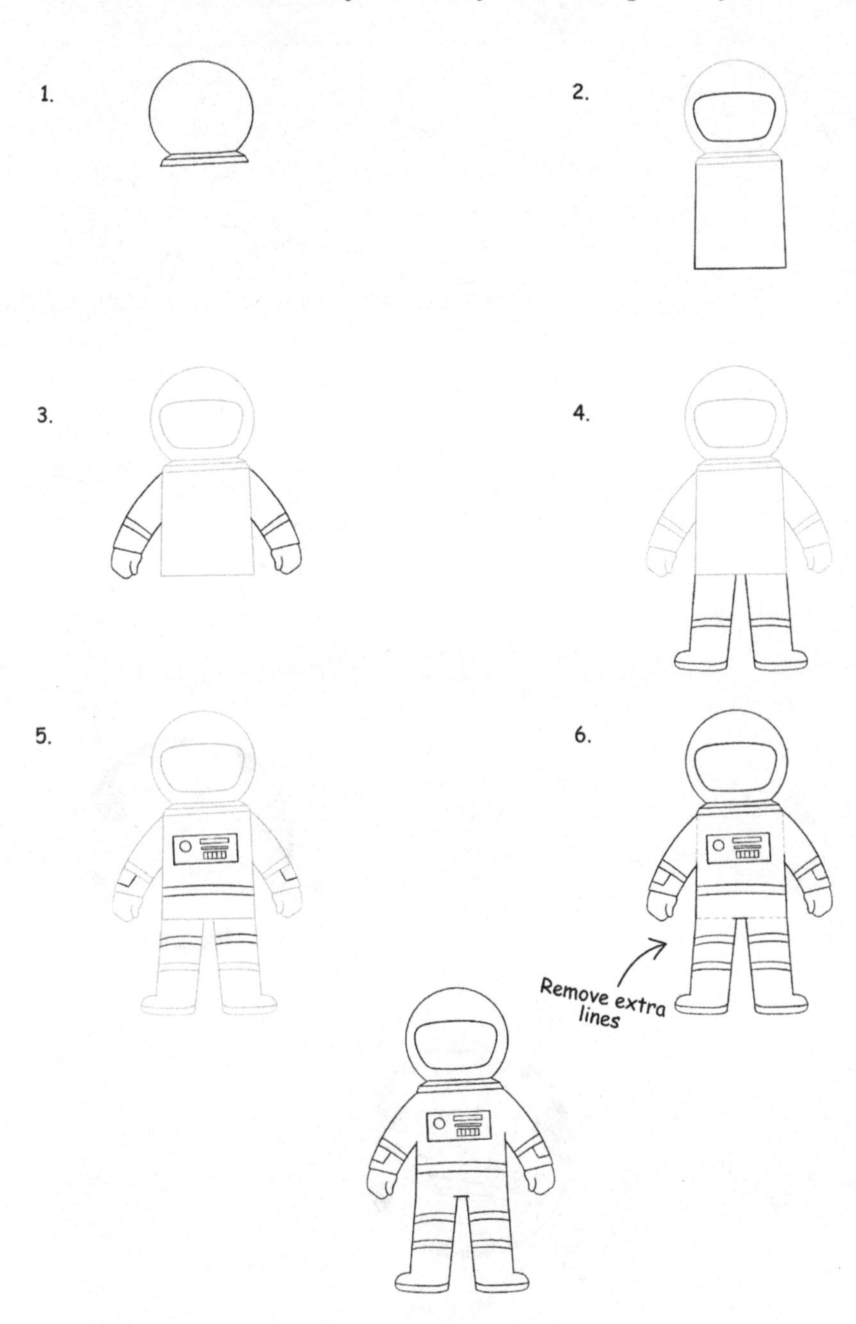

Planet

Our solar system has eight planets: Mercury, Venus, Earth, Mars, Jupiter, Saturn, Uranus, and Neptune. Earth is the only planet with life because it has water, air, and the right temperature for living things.

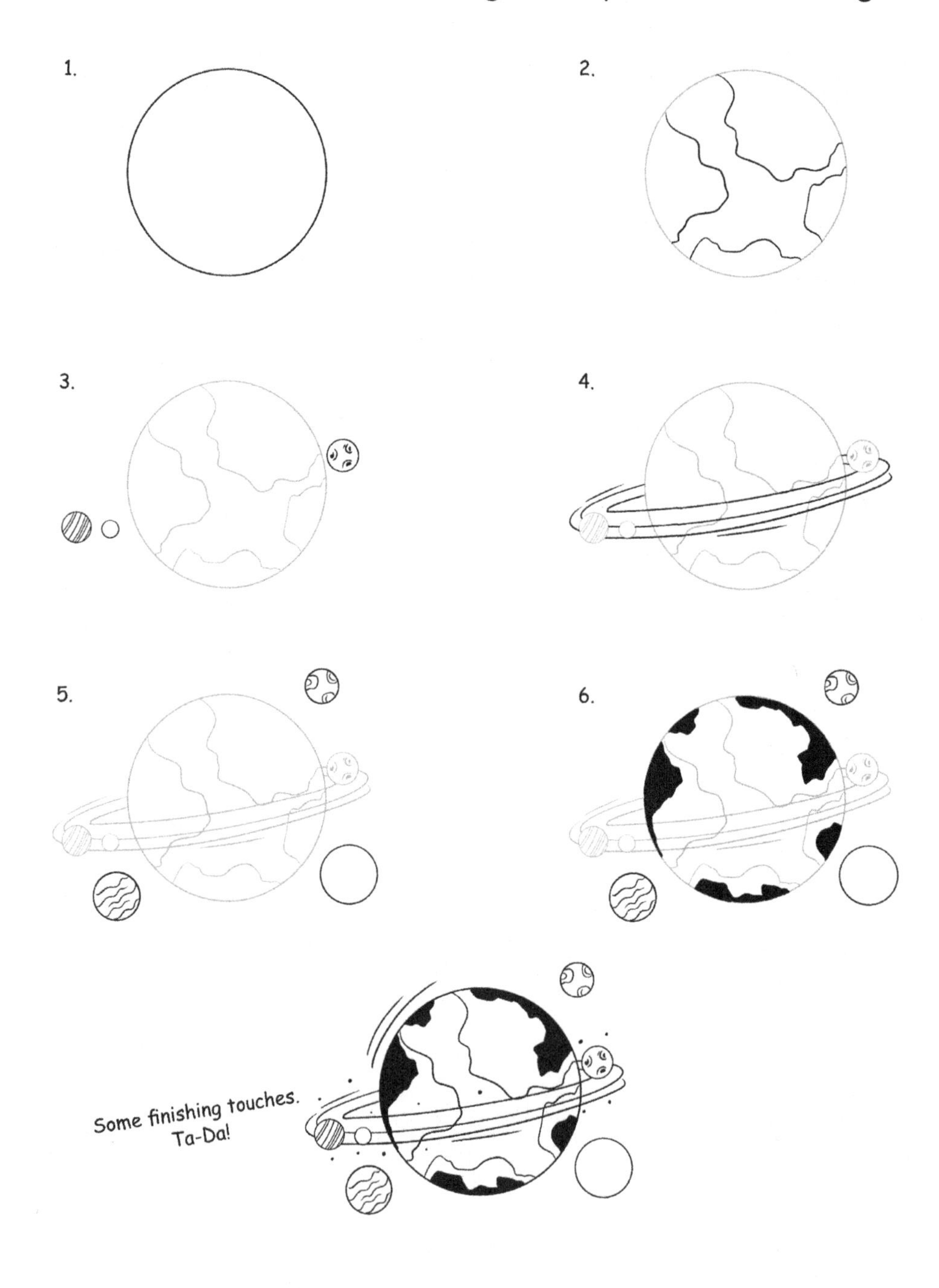

Satellite

Satellites are machines that orbit around Earth. They help with things you do every day, like watching your favorite TV shows or talking to someone on the phone. They even help predict the weather.

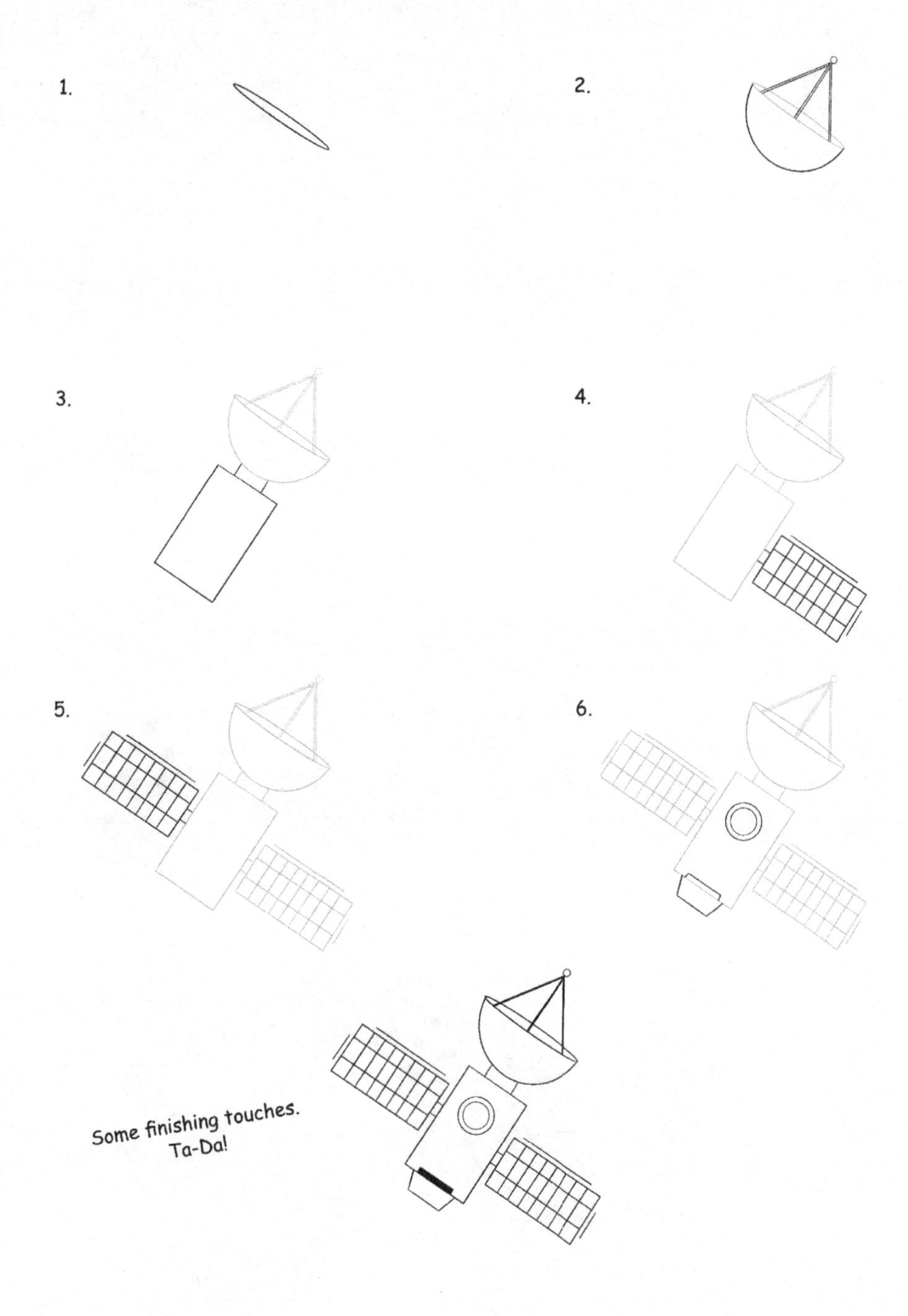

Comet

A comet is like a “dirty snowball” in space! It’s made of ice, dust, and gas. When a comet gets close to the Sun, the heat makes it melt and form a bright, glowing tail that can stretch for millions of miles!

1.

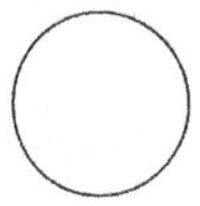

2.

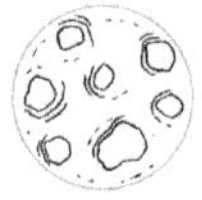

3.

4.

5.

6.

Alien

Aliens are creatures that some people think might live on other planets or in faraway galaxies. We haven't found any real aliens yet, but scientists believe life could exist in the vast universe.

1.

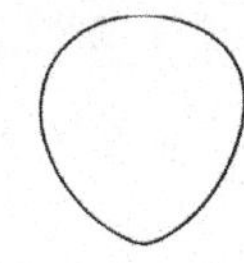

2.

3.

4.

5.

6.

Spaceship

A spaceship is a special vehicle that travels in space, going beyond Earth's atmosphere to explore places like the Moon and Mars. They also transport astronauts and cargo to the International Space Station.

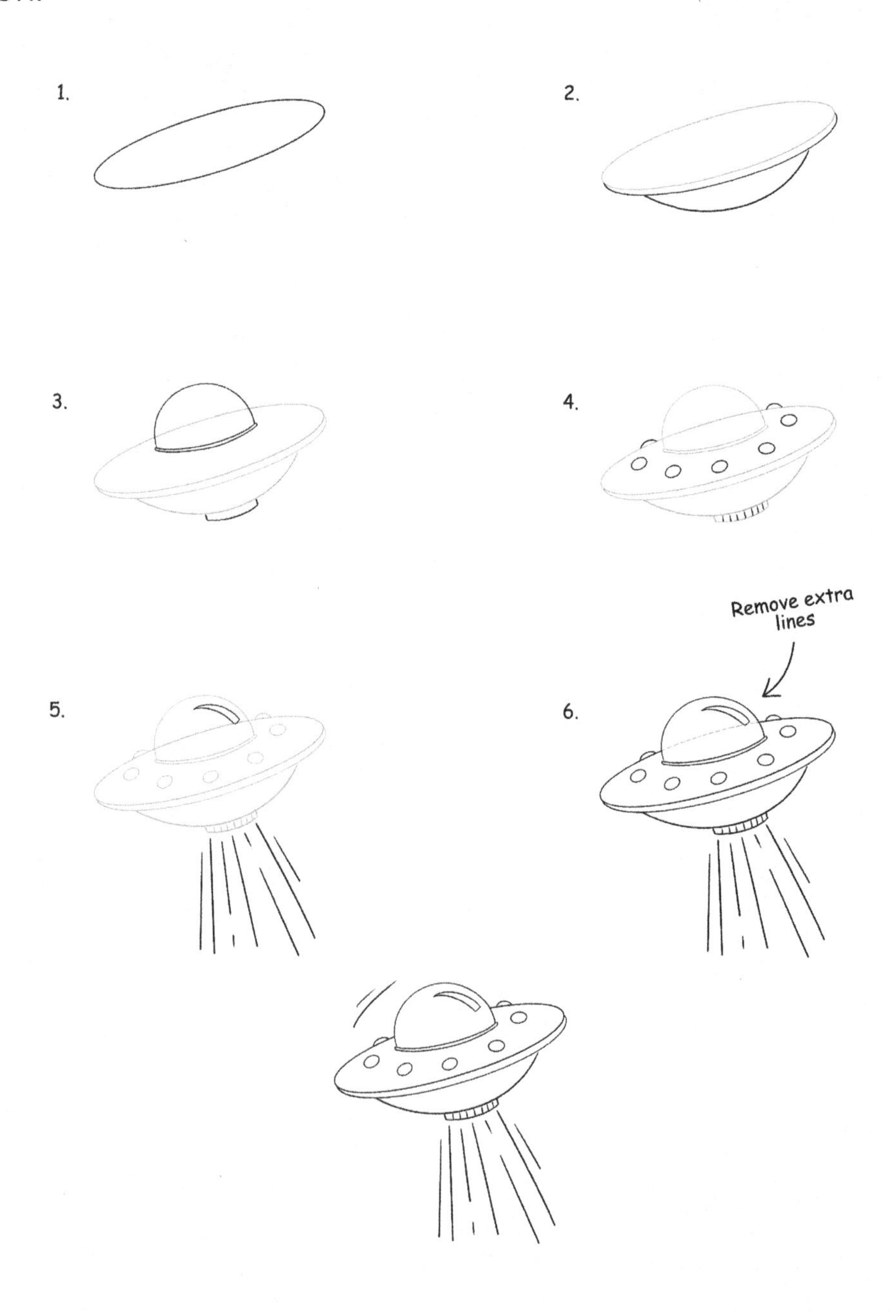

Moon

The Moon is Earth's only natural satellite, going around our planet. It's also the only place beyond Earth where humans have set foot. In 1969, Neil Armstrong and Buzz Aldrin were the first to step on the Moon.

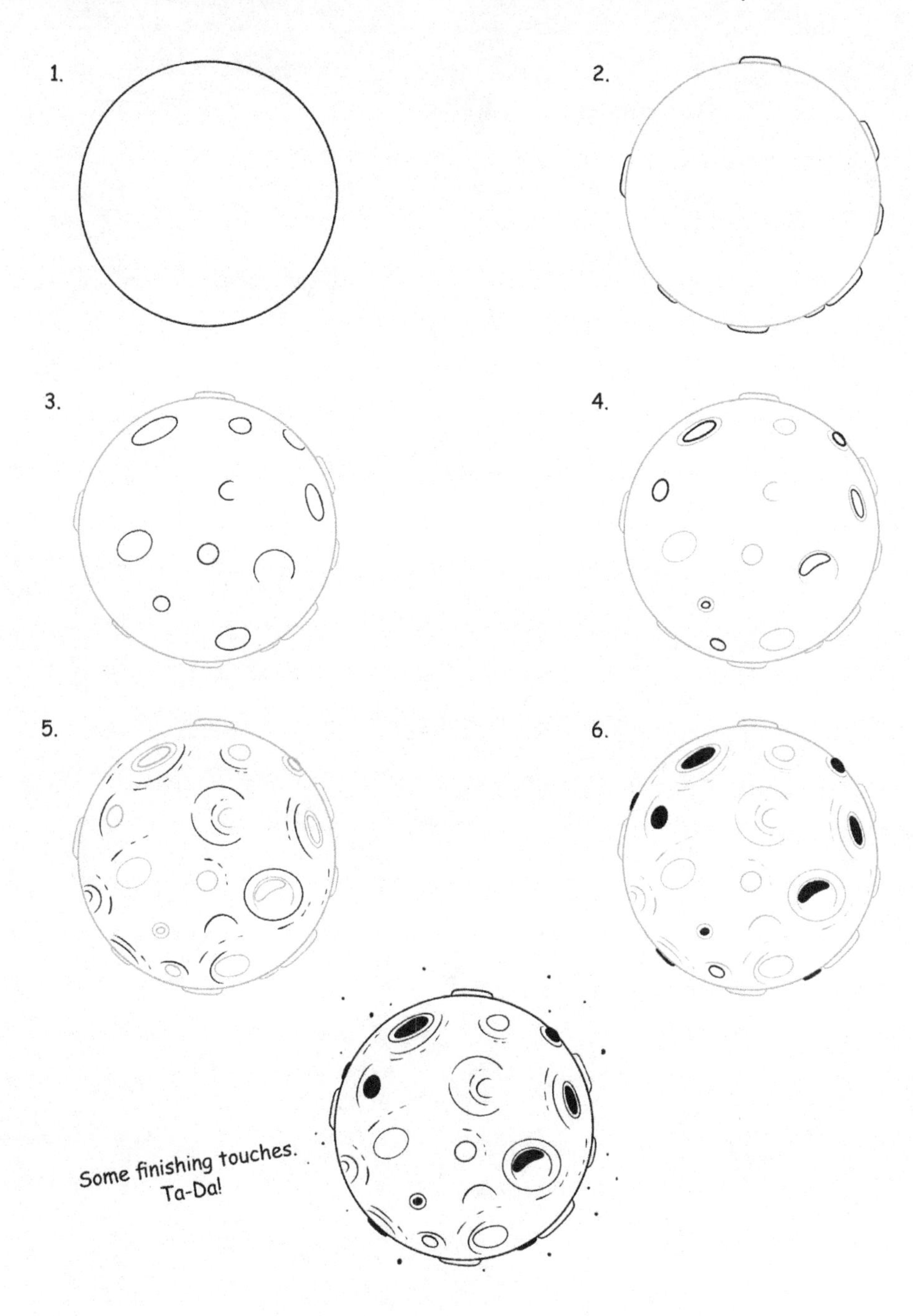

Stars

Stars are giant balls of hot gas that shine in the night sky. The closest star to Earth is the Sun, which provides us with light and warmth. Without the Sun, life on our planet would be impossible!

1.

2.

3.

4.

5.

6.

Some finishing touches.
Ta-Da!

Galaxy

A galaxy is a huge collection of stars, planets, dust, and gas held together by gravity. Our galaxy, the Milky Way, is shaped like a spiral and contains billions of stars, including our Sun!

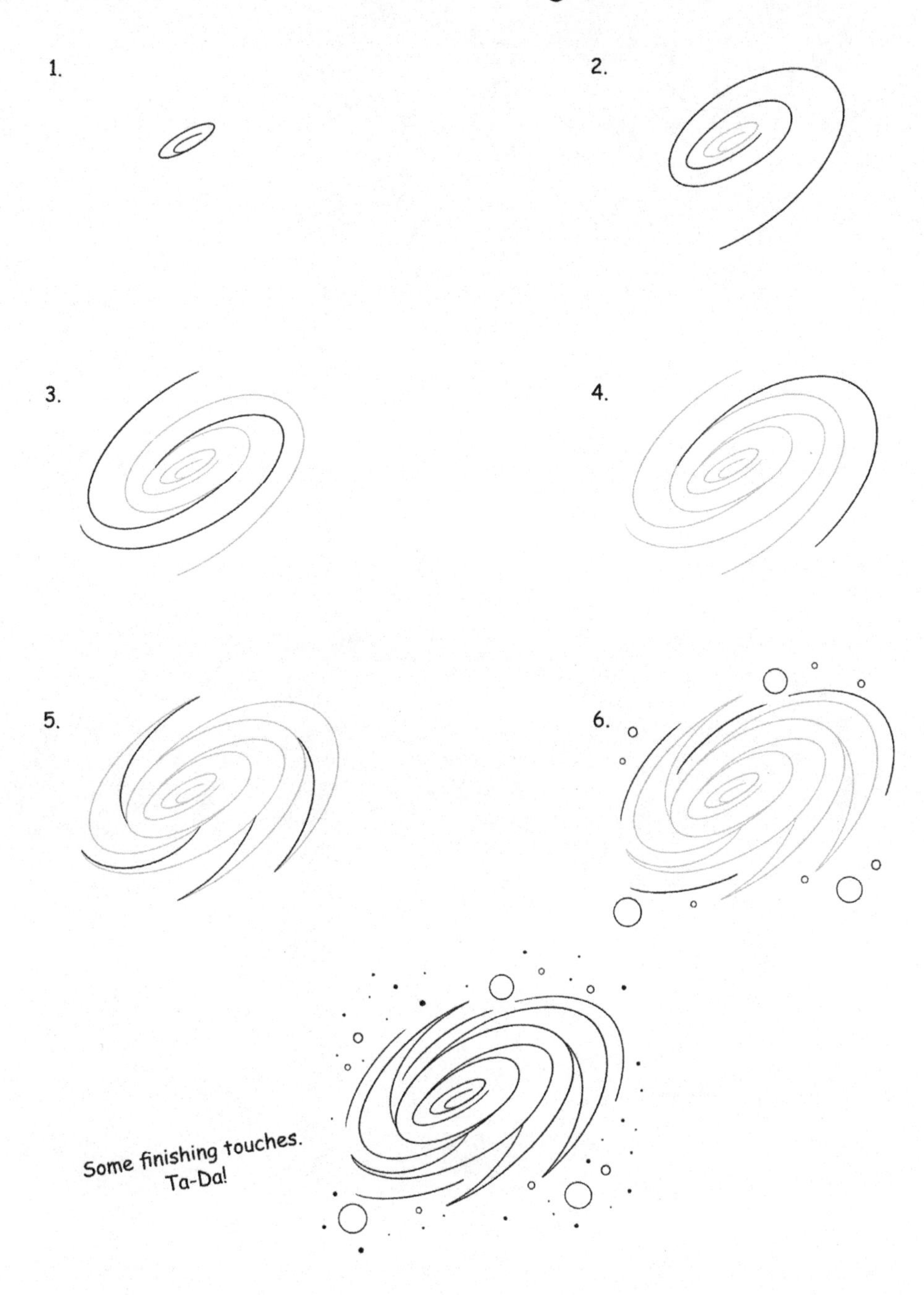

Now it's your turn

Now it's your turn

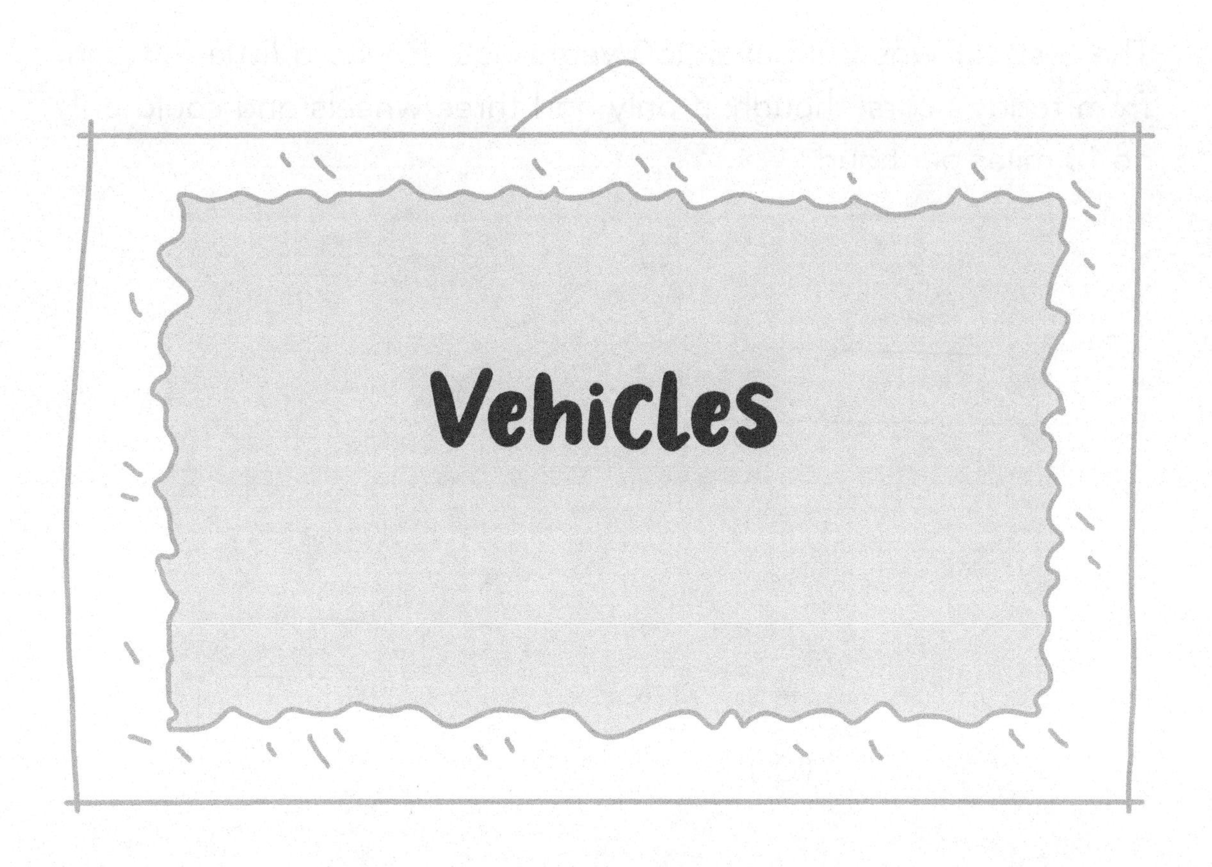

Vehicles

Car

The first car was built over 130 years ago. It was a little different from today's cars, though; it only had three wheels and could only go 10 miles per hour!

1.

2.

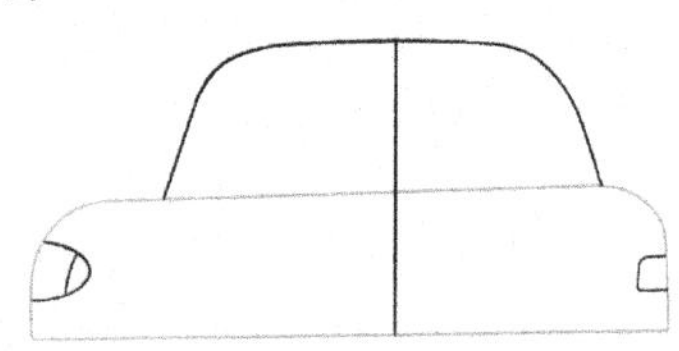

3.

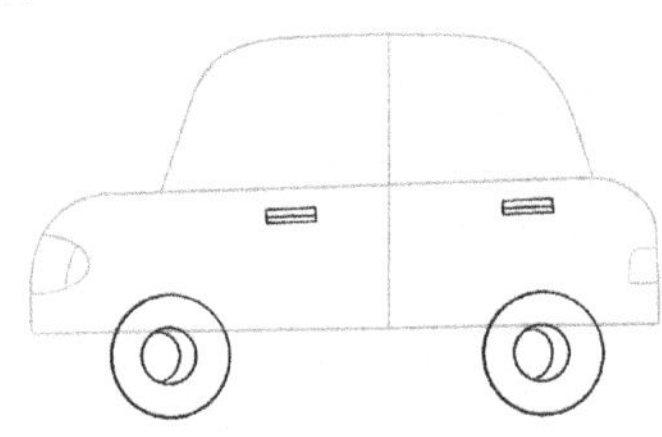

4.

5.

6.

Boat

The largest boats in the world are cruise ships, and some can carry over 6,000 passengers! They're like floating cities with restaurants, pools, and even theaters on board!

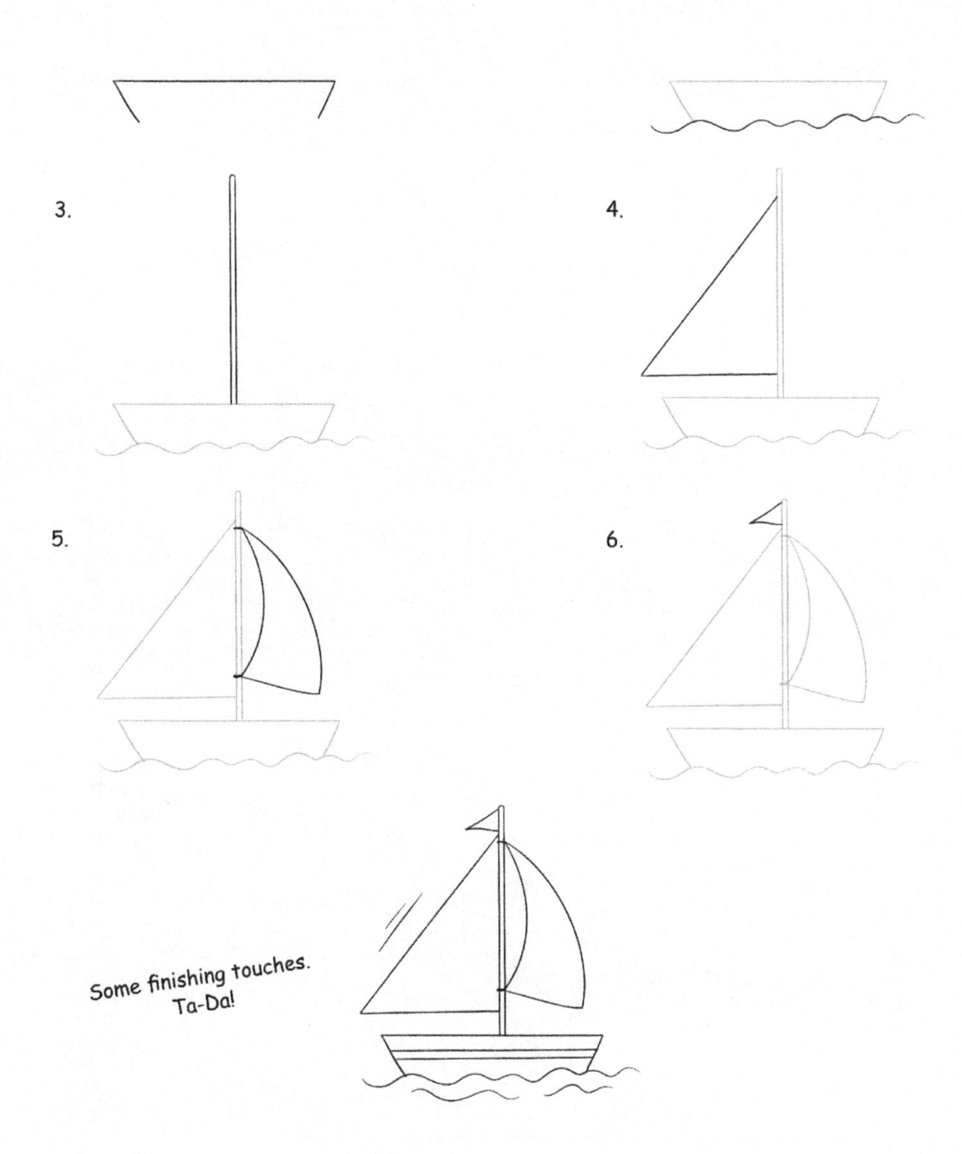

Airplane

The Wright brothers made the first powered airplane flight in 1903! Their plane flew for 12 seconds and covered 120 feet, which is about the length of a classroom!

1.

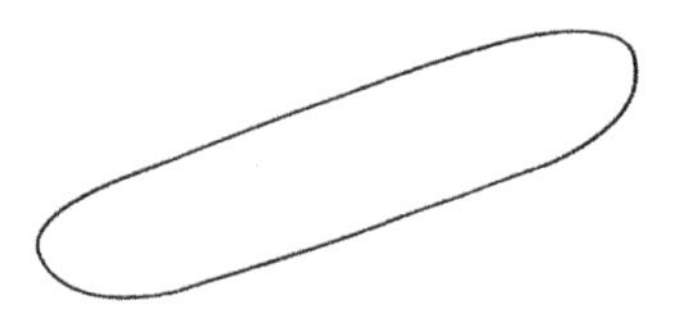

2.

3.

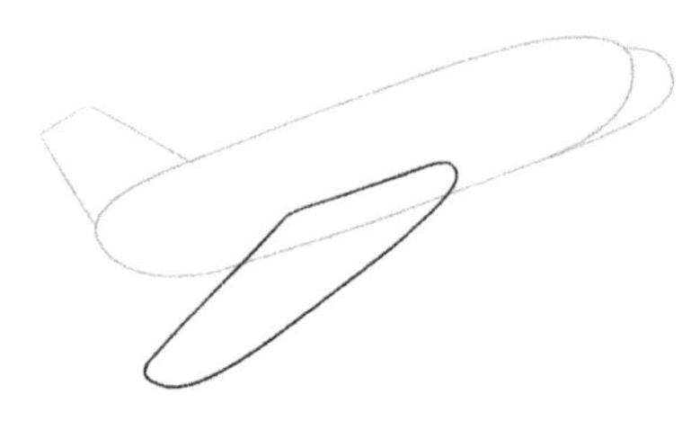

4.

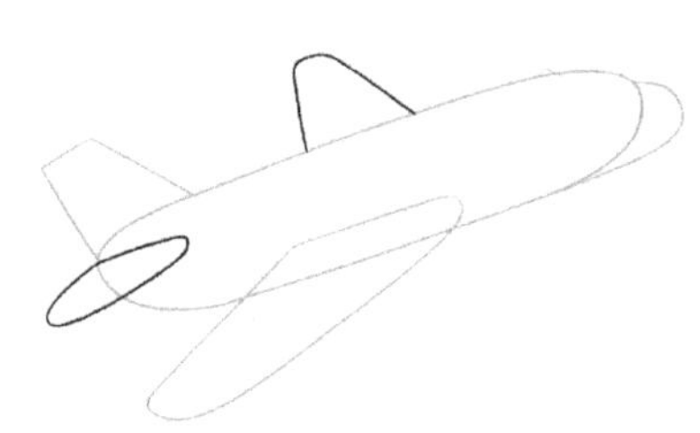

5.

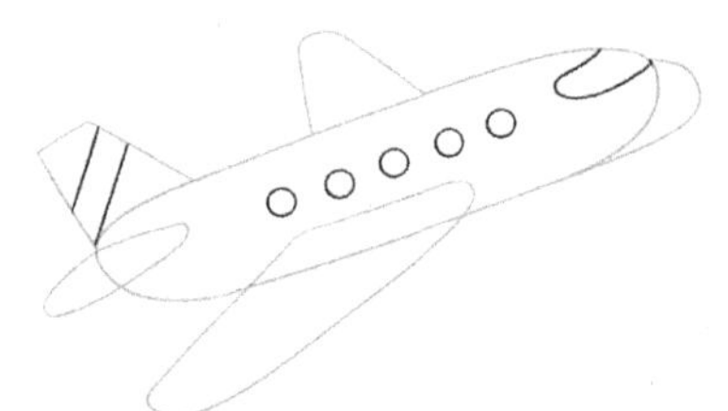

6.

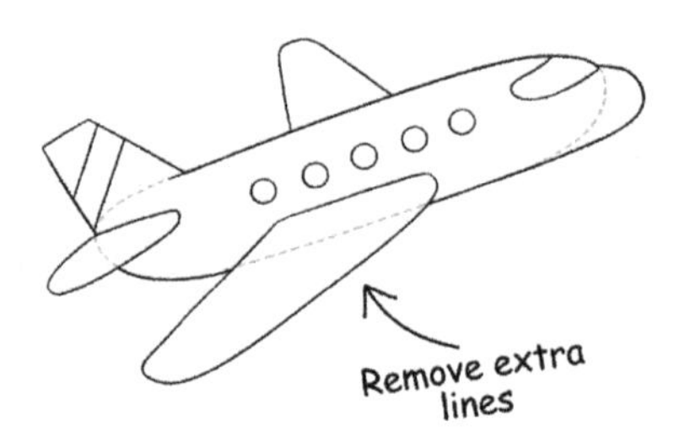

Some finishing touches.
Ta-Da!

Train

The first trains were powered by steam engines, which used coal and water to make steam and move the train.

1.

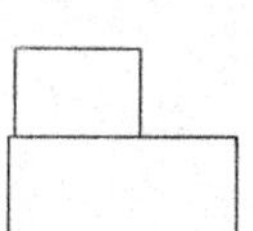

2.

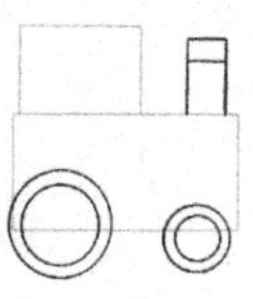

3.

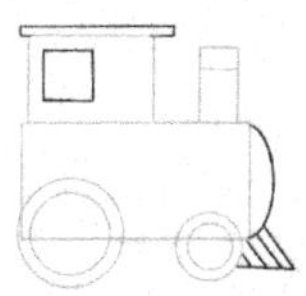

4.

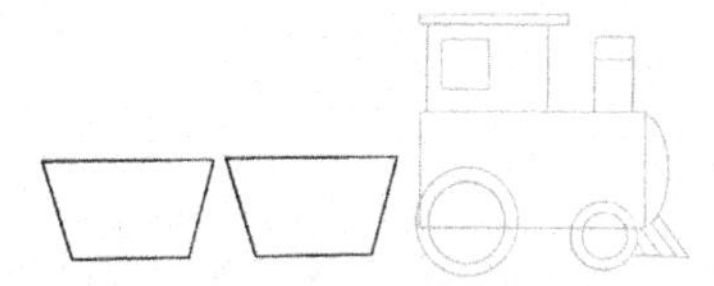

5.

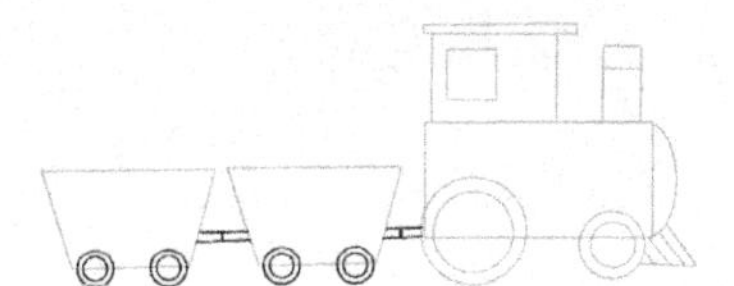

6.

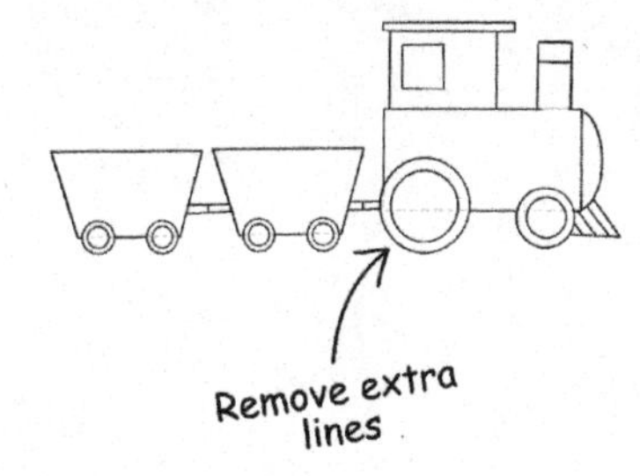

Some finishing touches. Ta-Da!

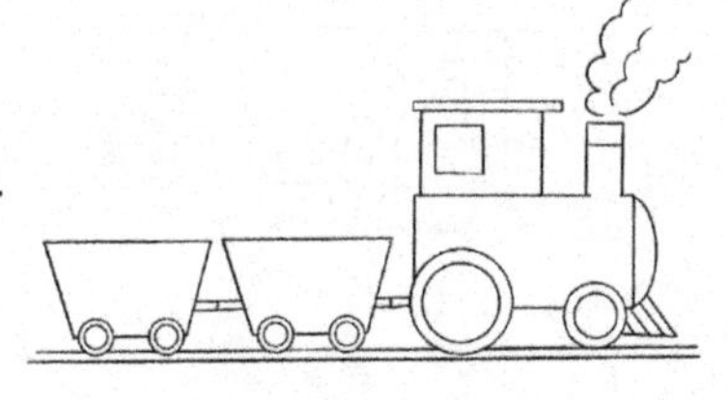

Helicopter

Helicopters work by using big, spinning blades on top called rotors. When the rotors spin really fast, they push air down, which lifts the helicopter into the sky.

1.

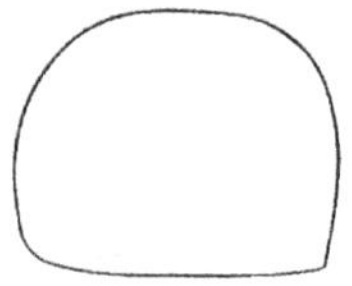

2.

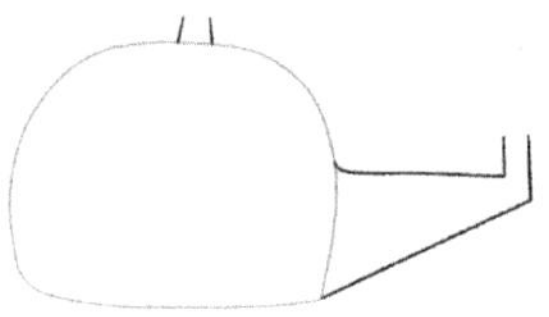

3.

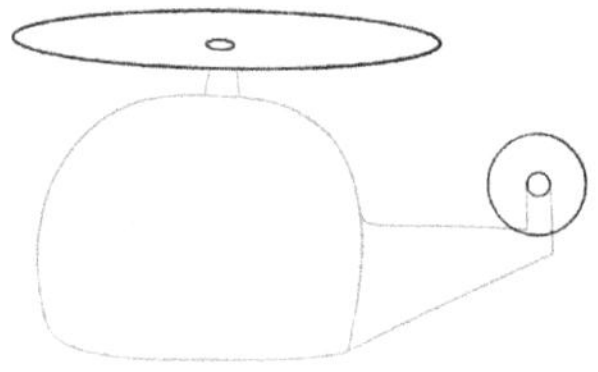

4.

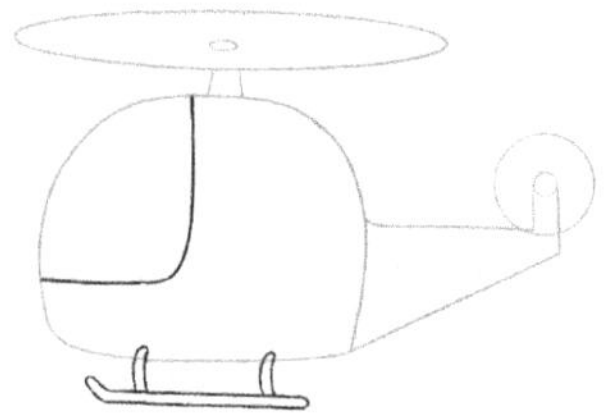

5.

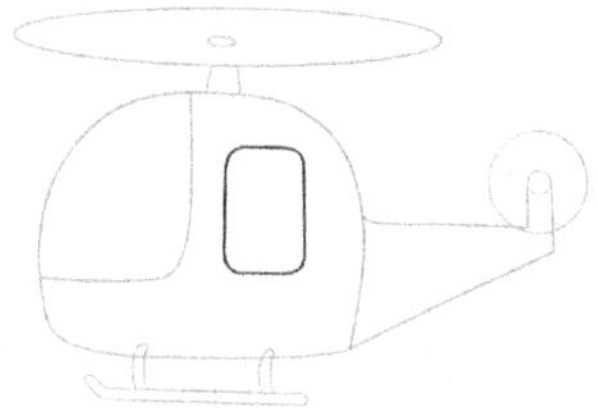

6.

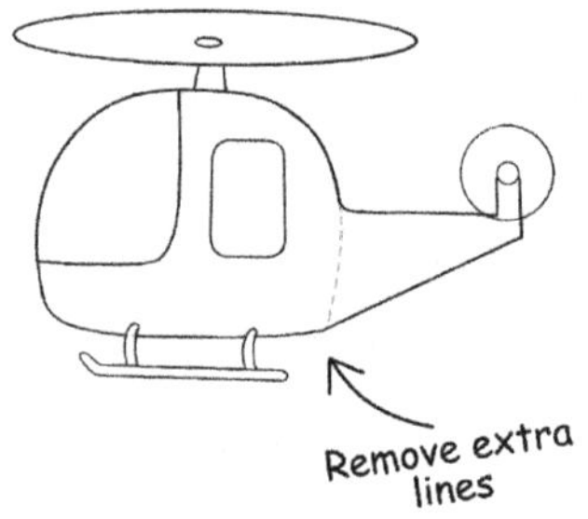

Remove extra lines

Some finishing touches.
Ta-Da!

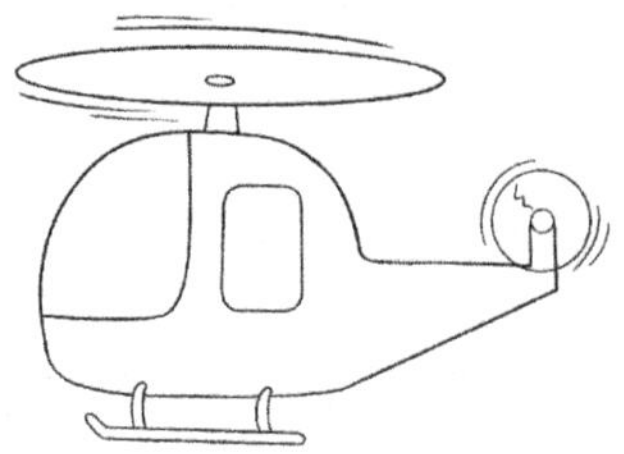

Bus

Do you take a bus to school? Imagine riding for 88 hours! That's how long it takes to travel the Greyhound bus route in America, which stretches from Miami, Florida, to Seattle, Washington. Now that's a journey!

1.

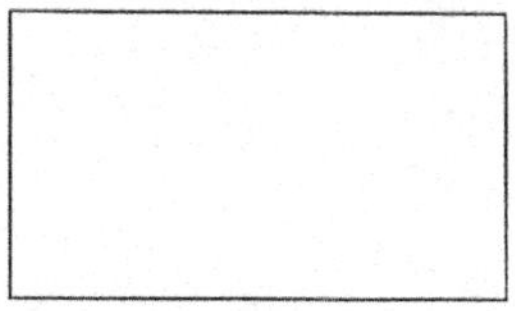

2.

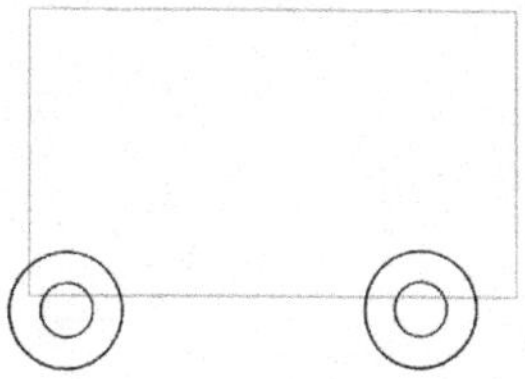

3.

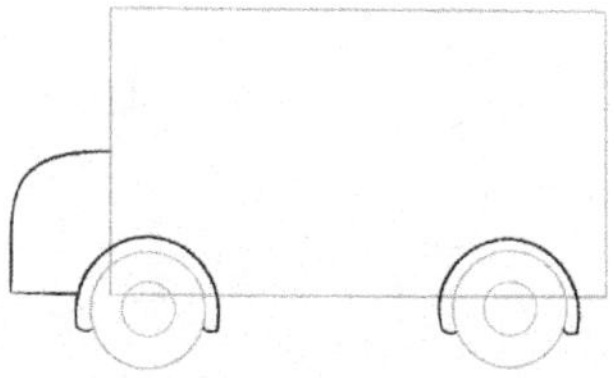

4.

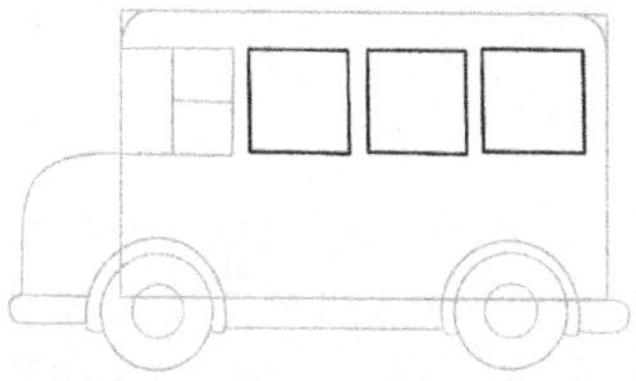

5.

6.

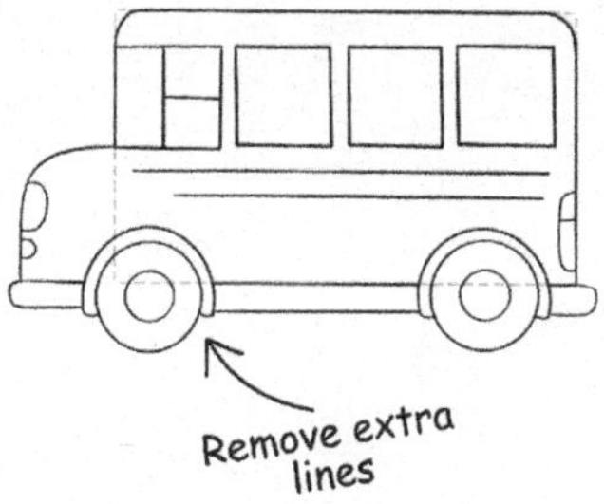

Remove extra lines

Some finishing touches. Ta-Da!

Tractor

Tractors have big wheels to drive over bumpy fields and can use different tools, like plows and mowers, making them super useful for farm work.

1.

2.

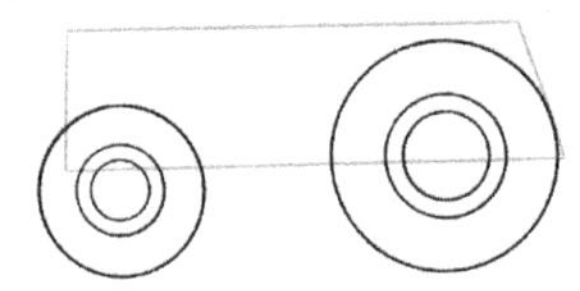

3.

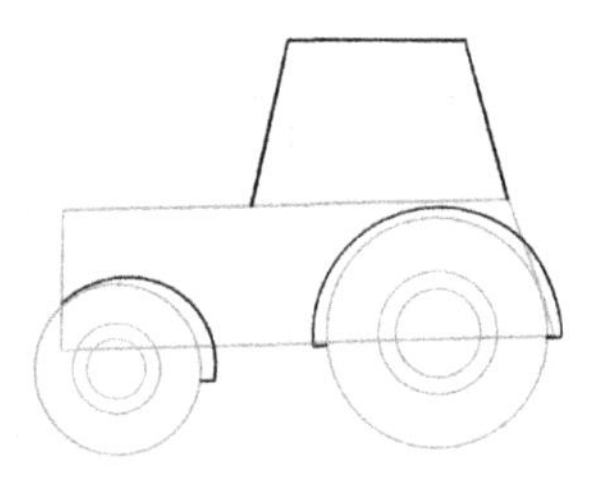

4.

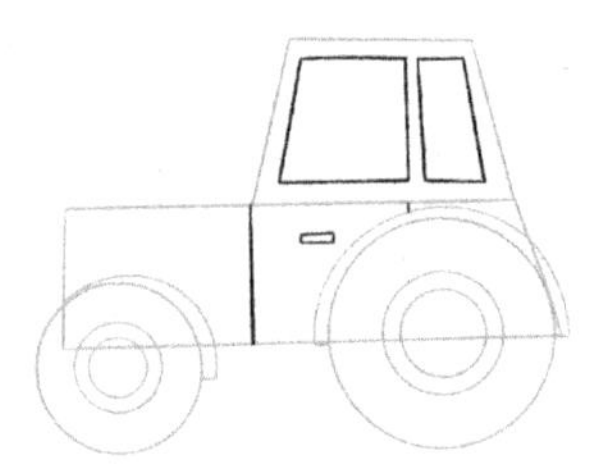

5.

6.

Some finishing touches. Ta-Da!

Scooter

Motor scooters are smaller and lighter than motorcycles, making them easy to ride, especially in busy cities. They can zoom around at 30-40 miles per hour!

1.

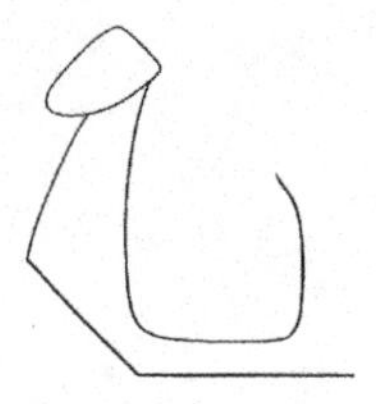

2.

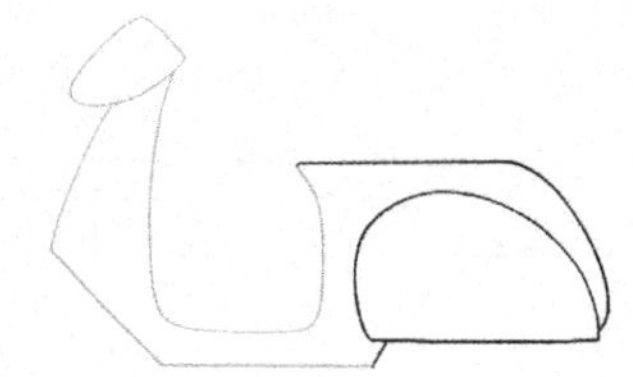

3.

4.

5.

6.

Fire Truck

Fire trucks are super strong and can carry heavy equipment, including ladders that can stretch over 100 feet high. These tall ladders help firefighters reach tall buildings and rescue people during emergencies.

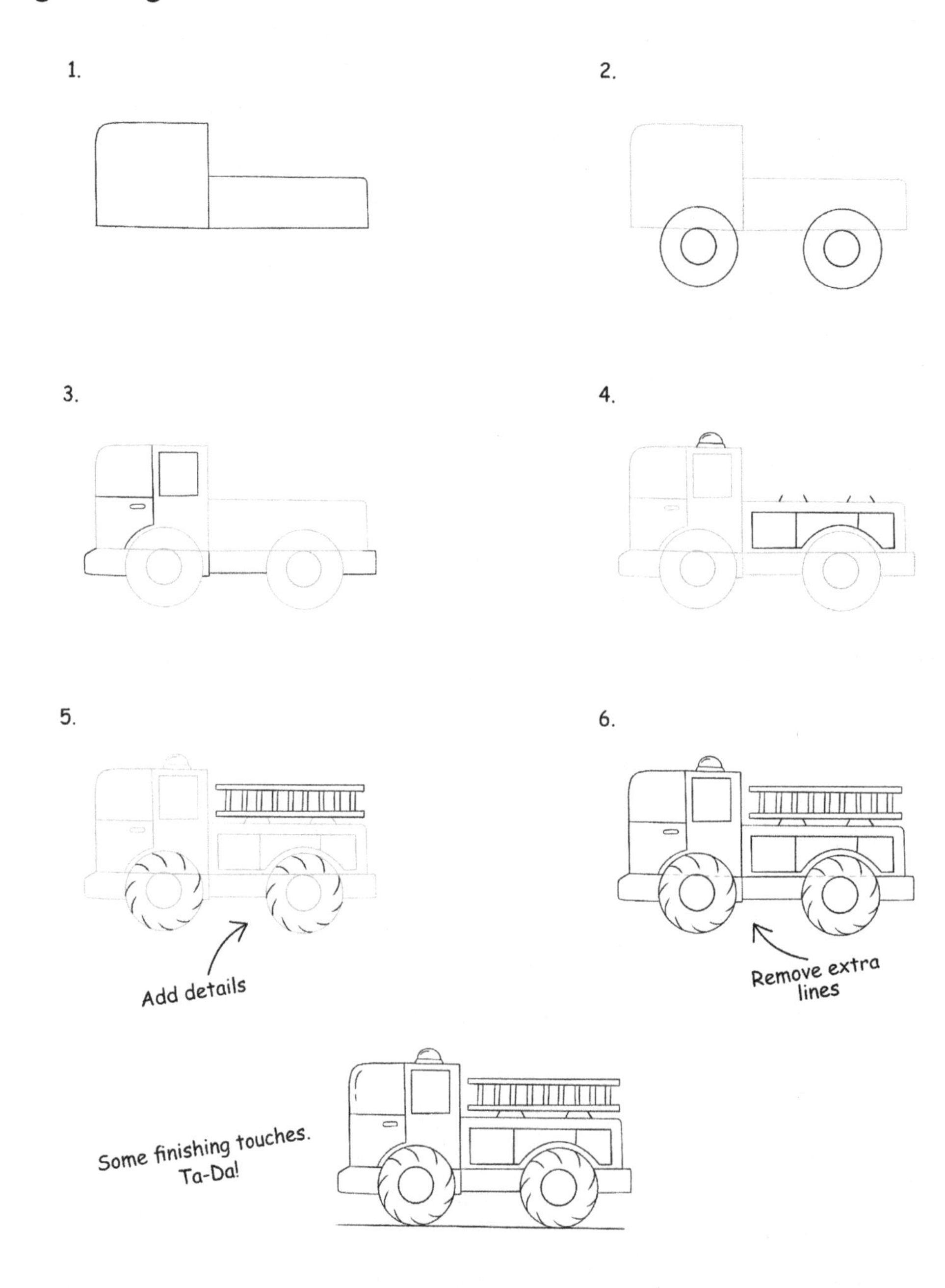

Submarine

Submarines are special boats that can travel deep underwater, staying hidden for long periods, which makes them perfect for secret navy missions.

1.

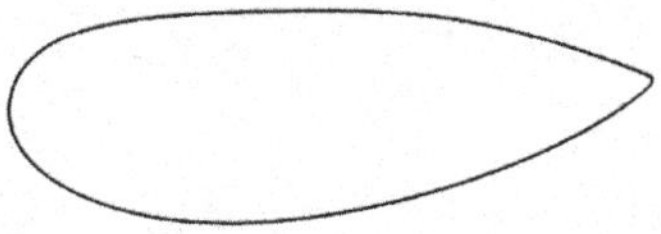

2.

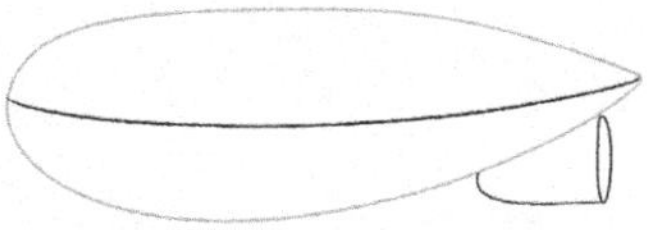

3.

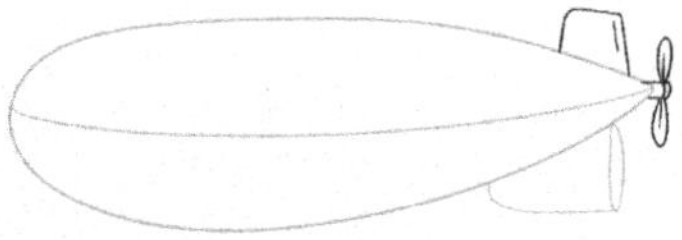

4.

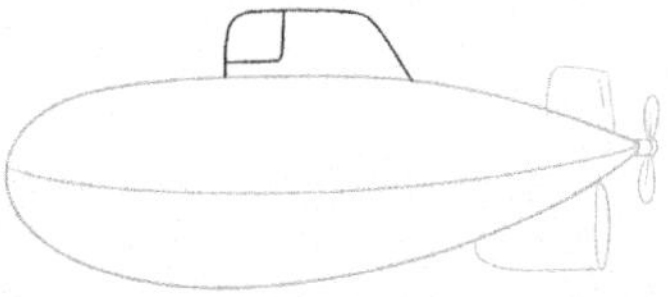

5.

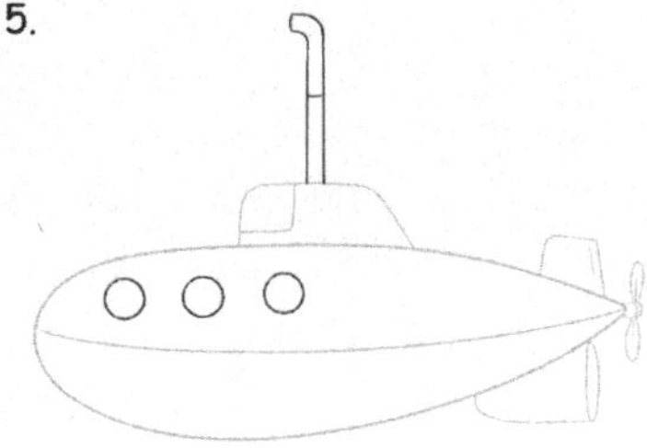

6.

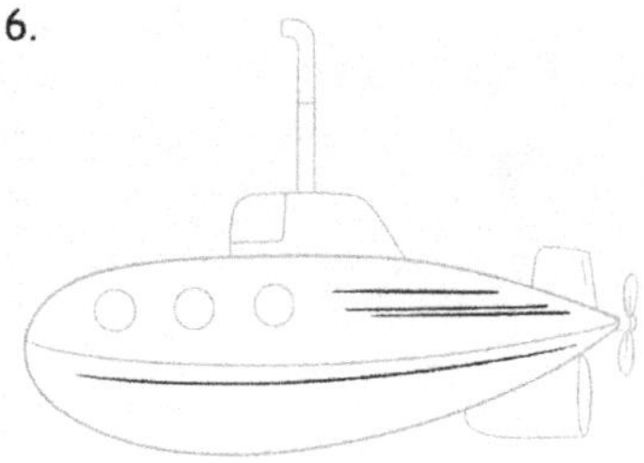

Some finishing touches.
Ta-Da!

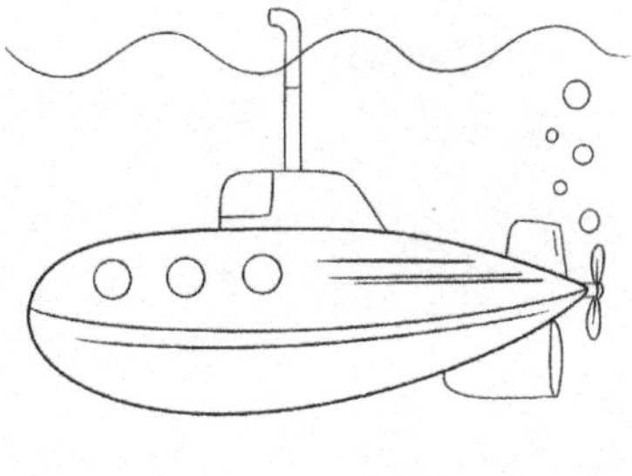

Now it's your turn

Now it's your turn

Nature

Tree

Trees can grow super tall, like the giant sequoias that reach over 300 feet! They provide homes for animals like birds and squirrels, and they help us breathe by giving us oxygen.

Flower

Flowers come in all shapes and sizes, and they can be found all over the world. They produce nectar that bees love to collect. In return, bees help flowers by spreading their pollen, which helps new flowers grow.

1.

2.

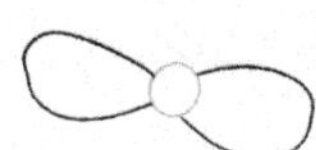

3.

4.

5.

6.

Some finishing touches.
Ta-Da!

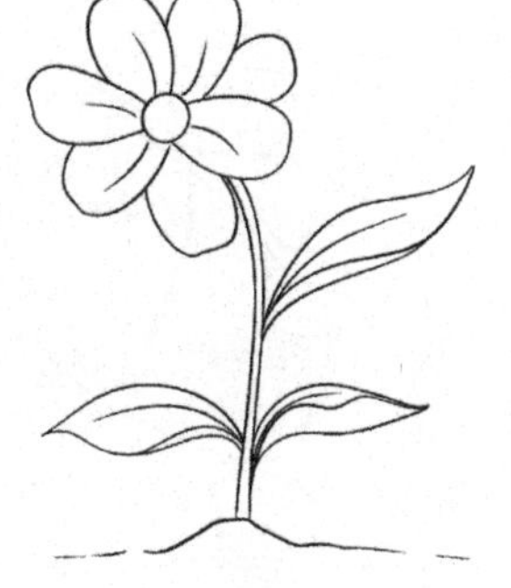

Leaf

Leaves are like tiny food factories for plants. They use sunlight, air, and water to make food and give us oxygen to breathe, helping keep the air clean!

1.

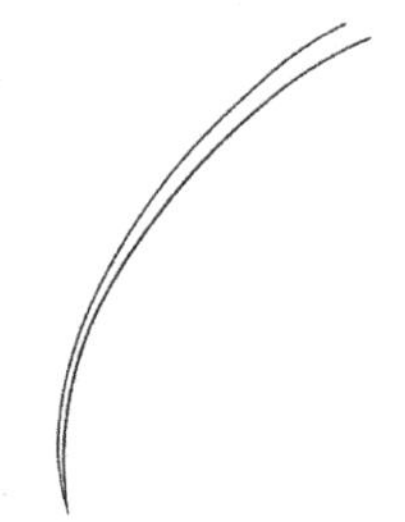

2.

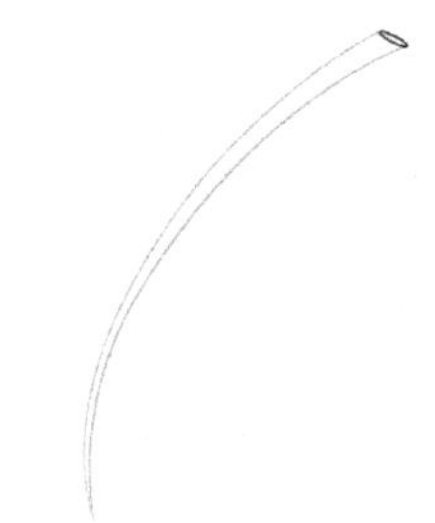

3.

4.

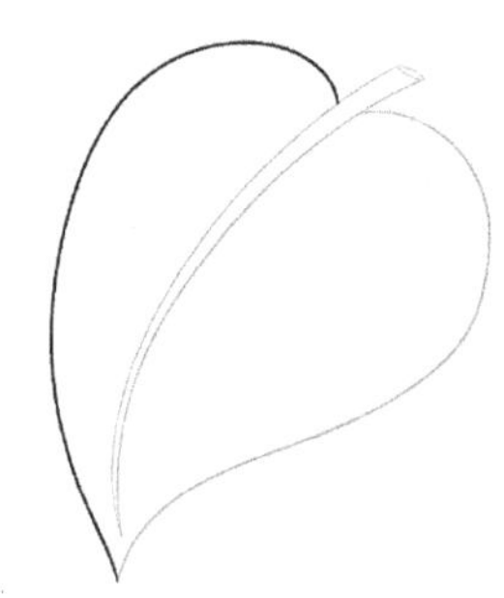

5.

6.

Mushroom

Mushrooms aren't plants — they belong to a special group called fungi. Unlike plants, which need sunlight to grow, mushrooms don't need sunlight at all.

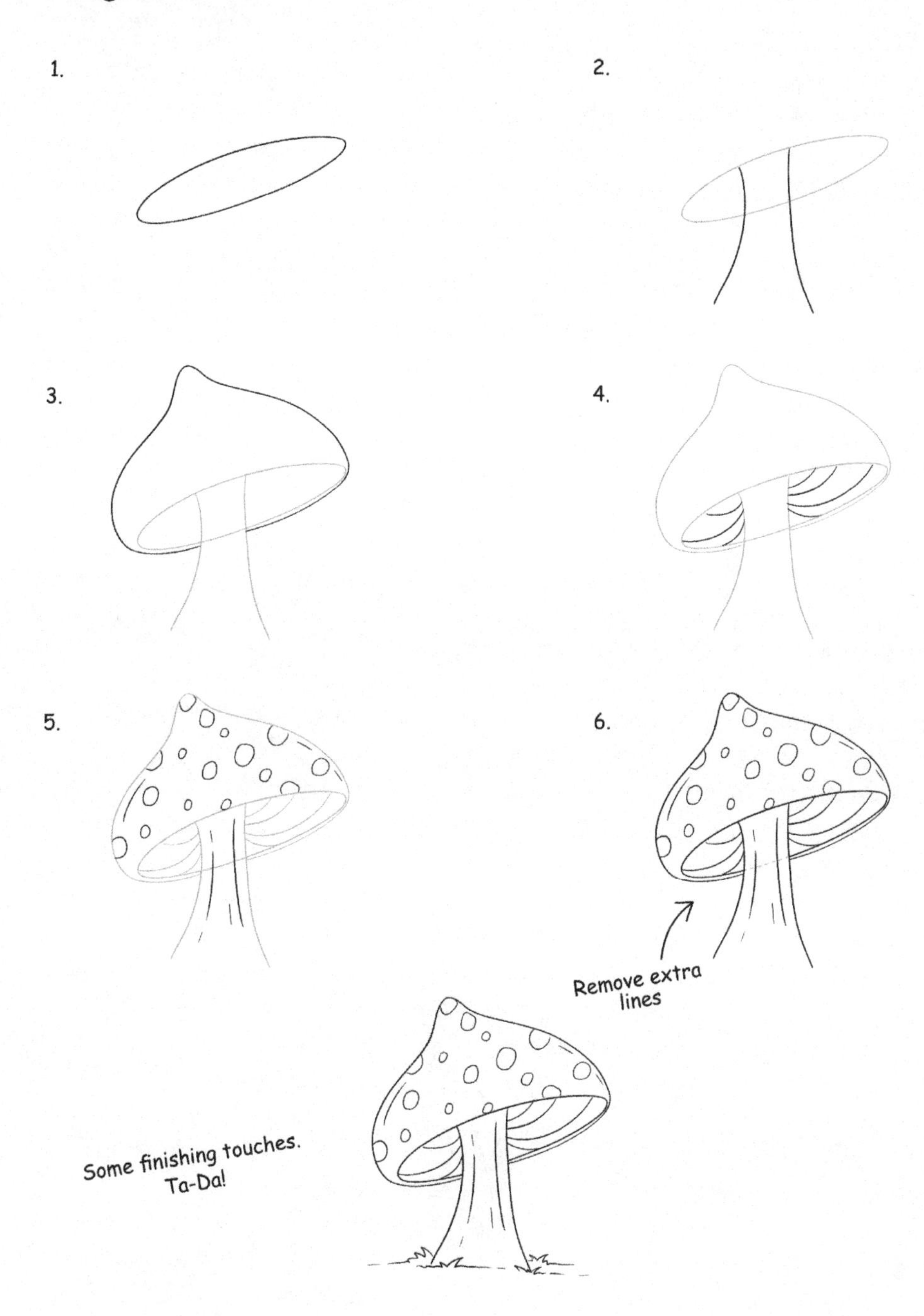

Sunflower

Sunflowers can grow very tall, sometimes taller than a grown-up, with big, bright yellow petals that look like the sun!

1.

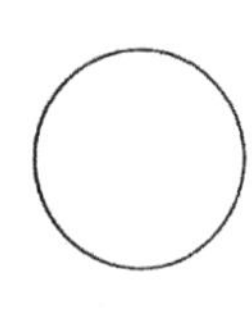

2.

3.

4.

5.

6.

Cactus

Cacti are plants that live in the desert, where it's really hot and dry. They're super tough and can survive for months without water by storing it in their thick stems.

Christmas Tree

Christmas trees are evergreen, which means they stay green all year. Over 500 years ago in Germany, people started decorating them with candles, fruits, and ornaments to celebrate the holidays.

1.

2.

3.

4.

5.

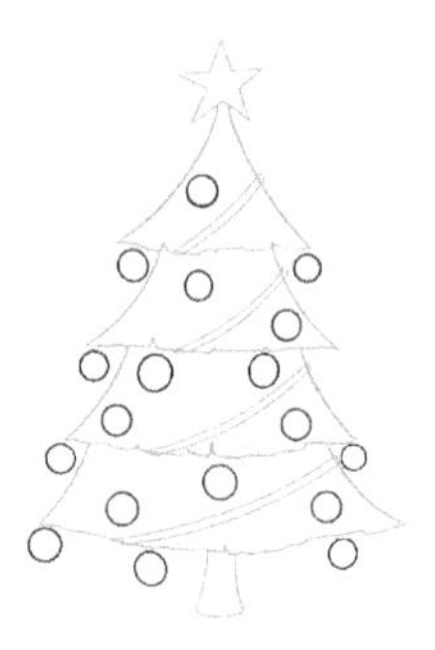

6.

Some finishing touches. Ta-Da!

Mountain

The tallest mountain in the world is Mount Everest, which is part of the Himalayas. People from all around the world try to climb it every year, but it can be very challenging and dangerous.

1.

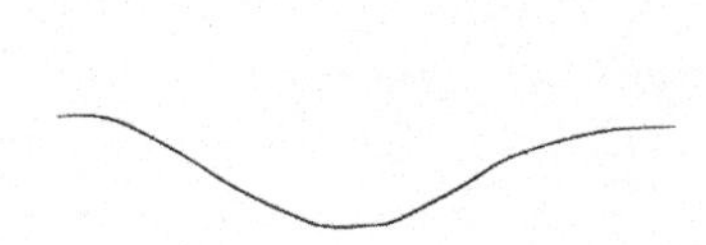

2.

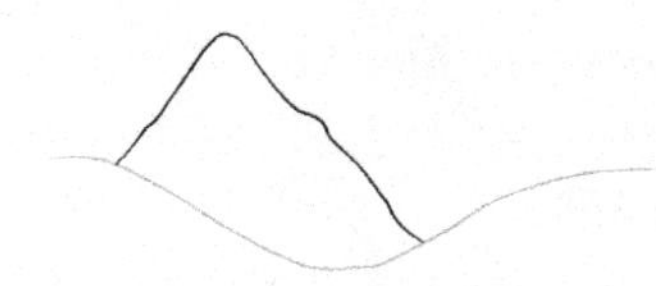

3.

4.

5.

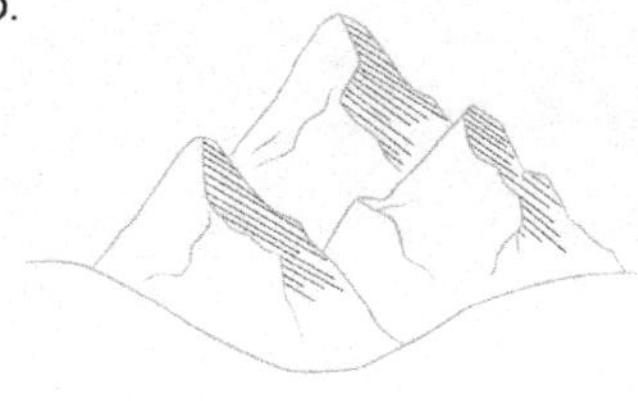

6.

Some finishing touches.
Ta-Da!

Now it's your turn

Now it's your turn

Now it's your turn.

Create your own masterpiece. Draw anything that inspires you—a favorite scene, an original character, or a beautiful landscape.

Made in the USA
Las Vegas, NV
16 December 2024